CW00669259

Systems He

The Man Who Invented Email
Unifies East & West to Reveal *The Science of Everything* on HOW
Your Body, Your Life, Your World is A System

The Science of Everything · Your Body Your System · Your System Your Life

V.A. Shiva PhD

The Inventor of Email

Dr. V. A. Shiva

To the Great Siddhars

Printed in the United States of America.

First Edition, 2016.

ISBN 978-0-9970402-8-9

General Interactive, LLC
Publishing Division
701 Concord Ave.
Cambridge, MA 02138
www.generalinteractive.com

All proceeds from the sale of this book go to Innovation Corps, a 501 (c) not-for-profit project.
www.innovation-corps.org

CONTENTS

The Science of Everything

The Man Who Invented Email Reveals the
Science That Interconnects Everything

INTRODUCTION

My journey to this book -- that is, to *The Science of Everything* -- began with a childhood passion for medicine.

That passion was originally inspired by watching my grandmother treat and heal people who lined up outside her home in Muhavur, a small village in South India. How did she do that? Where did she learn her skills? Could I learn them too?

Those questions led me on the long and winding path that I will revisit with you in these pages. Along that path, I earned four degrees at MIT in fields of engineering, architecture and biology. Then, disillusioned by the many problems I observed in conventional medicine, I studied various forms of traditional and alternative healthcare systems.

Still later, with the emergence of Systems Biology -- modern science's holistic approach to medicine -- my research in Systems Biology revealed connections across continents and centuries between modern systems theory, or more specifically control systems engineering, and the ancient healing science of Siddha.

In this connection I discovered the Science of Everything. In my research to integrate modern systems theory and ancient healing wisdom, I discovered the profound missing link between mind and body, and a common language that bridges the wisdom of East and West, ancient and modern, science and tradition. These discoveries are the foundations of this book, which will provide you a new understanding of what are the common principles that affect all systems in nature and reveal who you truly are.

When it comes to building a universal understanding of all things, "the theory of everything" is a phrase that comes up every once in awhile. You may have heard it in several different contexts. For instance, *The Theory of Everything* is the title of a film about the British physicist Stephen Hawking. The film stars Eddie Redmayne as the severely disabled scientist, and Felicity Jones as his wife. Eddie Redmayne won an Oscar for his role, and the film was also nominated for Best Picture.

The title of the film is also a reference to a problem in physics which has challenged Hawking, and has been a fundamental problem in science since the early 20th century. Albert Einstein was preoccupied with it for most of his later life.

Put very simply, the problem in physics involves integrating Einstein's theory of gravitation -- which describes space, time, and matter on the vast scale of the whole universe from planets to galaxies -- with quantum mechanics, which deals with the smallest possible scale of elementary particles. So far no one in physics has been able to describe or demonstrate the unity of the forces which traverse across these infinite spatial scales -- not Einstein, and not Stephen Hawking either.

But I have discovered the Science of Everything, although I'm not a physicist. And, what I'm going to share with you reveals a common set of principles that affects all systems from the infinitesimal to the infinite.

In fact, not being a physicist is the reason I was able to make that discovery. I'm an engineer, and as an engineer, I'm not oriented toward decades of abstract speculation in a university. Engineers have to build things that work. Doing that requires a practical set of principles that can be universally applied.

That set of principles exists in modern systems theory, which began to emerge as a specific scientific field in the 1930s. Systems theory really can be applied to everything, as you'll learn in the chapters that follow. Systems theory is a powerful unifying tool through which literally anything can be understood -- anything from biology to economics to human history and, especially, human health.

As I studied systems theory at MIT and later applied it in my work, I made an astonishing discovery that is actually an extension of systems theory as a unifying force. I realized that the ancient Indian wisdom tradition called Siddha, developed more than 5,000 years ago, expresses a unifying perspective that modern systems theory is now replicating.

The foundations of Siddha, the world's first application of systems thinking, are the same as the foundations of today's Control Systems Engineering --- the engineering principles that are the foundation of

13

nearly every major engineering development. The terminology may be different, but the results are the same. This is not just a *theory* of everything. It's a science and its practical application. In this book, you'll learn what those principles are and how to apply the Science of Everything to benefit your own life.

But who am I to have succeeded where Einstein and Hawking failed?

My personal background, detailed in Part One, *Journey to Systems*, provides a glimpse into the impetus for that success. From my birth, I was exposed to *systems* --- systems of oppression as well as systems of truth. My journey to understand the nature of those systems --- a journey in many ways motivated not by conscious choice --- is at the heart of my work as a scientist, inventor and revolutionary. I say revolutionary because my intent is to destroy those long-standing systems of oppression, and to create and rediscover those systems that bring truth, freedom and health. In my other books, I also include this Part as a core module of the content in order to provide you insights of how the path I traversed directly motivated my fascination with systems. If you've read it before, you can skip to Part Two.

Part Two will start in the West with my training in systems biology --- the end of a journey across those four degrees from MIT. You will be introduced to the principles of the emerging field of systems biology --- a new field which aims to address many of the problems with the reductionism of western biology. This will provide you the foundation to understand that the West's recent inspiration for a systems-based approach to biology is what others in the East traversed many millennia ago.

Part Three discusses the core principles of Siddha, which are revealed not only as an ancient wisdom tradition, but also as a striking and modern holistic model of our environment on every scale from the largest to the smallest, from the individual cell to the universe itself. This, you will learn, is truly "the first systems biology."

Part Four provides a detailed explanation of modern control systems engineering theory. This knowledge is what I learned at MIT. However, my attempt here is to bring this knowledge to you so you can easily understand and appreciate it, as well as its relevance, and how it operates in the physical world.

Part Five -- "The Rosetta Stone" -- reveals the fundamental link that I discovered during my Fulbright Research between the core principles of modern control systems engineering and the core principles of Siddha. This opens the door to the Science of Everything, at a time when Western science desperately needs to move beyond reductionism toward an engineering systems approach.

Part Six provides guidelines for self-identifying, using the Science of Everything, the interactions of systems elements in your own body, as well as tools for restoring health when those elements become unbalanced. Your body is the most easily accessible "laboratory" to see how the Science of Everything is in play all the time.

Finally, I've included Part Seven, where the Science of Everything goes to the movies! You will realize the truly universal applicability of the Theory not only to your body as a system but also to understand stories and movies as systems.

Onward!

PART 1

The Journey to Systems

CHAPTER 1

A Child of Oppression and Truth

Like most people, when I look back on my life I see things that seem obvious now, but were invisible when they were actually taking place. I see connections that were waiting to be recognized, but I had to learn to see and understand them.

I have a Ph.D. in systems biology from MIT, for example, but long before I studied the science of systems theory, I had already experienced the presence and power of systems throughout my life. Later in this book you'll learn much more about what systems are and what they can do. But for now, I'll just say that I was born into the caste system of India, I was also introduced as a child to the Indian system of medicine and its wisdom tradition known as Siddha, and later I spent a good amount of time in the caste system of American academia, business, and entertainment.

And, in 1978, I built the first email system and later had to endure the rage, collusion, and deplorable vitriol, starting in 2012 after my work was received by the Smithsonian, of those who sought to destroy me for my daring to assert my rightful place in history as the inventor of email. The truth of a 14-year-old, Indian immigrant boy inventing email in Newark, New Jersey was antagonistic to the priesthood of vested interests, "historians," and "internet pioneers" who wished to perpetuate their gated and well-defined caste system of when, where and by whom innovation could take place.

All of this, of course, has made the study of systems a major focus of my life and work -- but if someone were to ask me what conclusions I've come to regarding my experience with systems, I would have to say I have mixed feelings.

I have certainly seen the limiting and destructive effects of the Indian caste system, and also of the surprisingly similar system that exists in America. In fact, I want to do everything I can to reveal those systems for what they are and destroy them if possible. Yes, destroy them. If that sounds like a radical aspiration, that's exactly what I intend.

On the other hand, I have also seen how Siddha --- another system --- a 5,000 year old system of healing and spirituality, had enormous benefits both for both the physical well being and the spiritual health of the community. Watching my grandmother, who was a Siddha healer, was one of the most important experiences of my life. It showed me the practical benefits and spiritual wisdom that could exist in a system that pre-dated Western science by many centuries. It further showed me that none of this depended on the

19

conventional educational system, and definitely not on academic degrees. When I returned to India years later, I also realized how Siddha anticipated many of the elements of modern systems theory. The terminology was different, but the principles were the same.

There will be much more to say about all this throughout the book. But to begin, I was born in Bombay (now called Mumbai), a cosmopolitan and diverse metropolis with the largest population of any city in India. But I also spent large amounts of time in a small village called Muhavur where my grandparents lived. My grandparents were very small family subsistence farmers --- they tilled the Indian soil growing cotton, coconuts, peanuts and rice.

My grandmother worked in the fields for sixteen hours a day. As I've said, she was also a healer in the traditional Indian system of health called Siddha. This is one of the world's oldest healing systems, and it also anticipates and uses the modern systems approach that you'll learn about in a later chapter.

She could predict what was going on in a person's body simply by looking at that person's face. This skill or art is known in the ancient Indian Tamil treatises as *Samudkrika Lakshanam*. After she diagnosed someone, she could provide a healing modality -- it could include massage, or yoga, or a variety of herbs -- always in sync with the person's specific needs and identity. And that, by the way, is the direction that Western science is now trying to take. It's called *personalized medicine* or *precision medicine* --- giving the right treatment, at the right time, for the right person.

My understanding of the knowledge of Siddha and its teachers, known as Siddhars, began by observing my grandmother. Each morning, my grandmother, Chinnathai, would rise before sunrise and, following an ancient tradition, create beautiful drawings known as *kolams* on the ground in front of the entrance to the house. She used milled white rice flour that flowed through her hands, like sand passing through an hourglass, to make abstract geometric and symmetric designs, resembling mandalas.

The kolams served a dual purpose: The rice flour attracted ants and other insects and kept them from entering the home, but there was always a larger, more important, spiritual benefit for the artist and the viewer. Sometimes I would wake up early just to watch my grandmother drawing the daily kolam, a process that was indescribable, with visions emanating from her mind's eye onto the red brown earth. The designs were said to evoke the spiritual world and put one who looked upon them into higher states of consciousness.

Coming home, the kolams were reminders that one was entering a special place. Two solid teak doors were the entrance into a small 10-foot by 12-foot space, which served as the living room, dining room, and the first floor sleeping room. Ahead, one could see the kitchen, where something was always cooking. The fragrance of cumin, ginger, cardamom, red pepper, and freshly ground coconut filled the air. Pictures of the great deities and heroes lined the edge of where the four walls met the ceiling of the living room.

A powerful image of Shiva, my namesake, with the power to destroy, create, and transform; Rama, the virtuous and noble hero of the Ramayana; Devi, the mother Goddess; Parvathi, wife, loyal and devoted consort of Shiva; Ganesha, the elephant headed one who removed obstacles; Jesus, God's avatar and the Savior of mankind; Saraswati, the Goddess of knowledge; Lakshmi, the Goddess of wealth and others. The smell of subtle incense and holy ash was always in the air. My favorite was the deity Muruga, whose picture graced the small altar. Muruga was known as the teacher of teachers or yogi of yogis; the deity's familiar mount was the peacock and above the picture hung a beautiful single peacock feather.

My grandmother knew the ancient arts and was known to be clairvoyant; on occasion she would channel spirits. She had knowledge of the great herbs and medicines to be used for nearly any ailment, and would do rituals and mantras to heal those who requested. Her arms were marked with amazing tattoos. She had a nose ring. Her hair was pitch black and she chewed tobacco and betel leaf. Her face was like the earth, dark with hues of red, and eyes that extended to the beyond, and lines marking her journey across many life times. I thought everyone had a grandmother like her.

She had grown up in Burma, the land of cobras and Buddhism. After giving birth to my father, she did not have another child, something which, at the time, was seen as heresy. There was serious talk of marrying another woman to my grandfather. She and my dad, then five years old, made pilgrimages to many Buddhist temples seeking blessings. One monk with a face my father describes as "pure light," gave my father a mantra, a sacred sound, initiating him to meditation, along with a gold Burmese coin, and a promise that on December 2, he would have a brother. My uncle Siva was born exactly as predicted and to this day wears that Burmese coin as an amulet. My grandmother then went on to have six other children.

My great-grandfather, who I remember well, was also a hardworking farmer and was considered by local villagers also as a Swamiji, a spiritual Master or Adept, who could perform what we in the West would consider superhuman feats. He was her teacher and trained her in many of the ancient arts. My grandmother had a profound understanding of the power of observation and its ability to reveal Nature's hidden secrets. From her, I learned that all things in Nature are interconnected, and that our intentions are the source of our liberation or bondage.

Every day people would come to her house, asking for healing help; on weekends, long lines extended from her door. No one was refused; no payment was ever required. This was not her occupation; her "day job" was working in the rice and cotton fields to make ends meet. My grandmother often talked to me about healing. She said to heal people one had to have the attitude of a warrior with a desire to serve; she said that being able to serve others was a gift from God.

She was the youngest of sixteen children—the only daughter—and the last remaining member of her family; all her siblings had died. She adored her father, who she described as Robin Hood. He literally stole from the rich and gave to the poor, and was beloved by all. She loved to tell me stories of him and the great epics of Indian lore, of Gods and Demons, good and evil, how virtue and honor always overcame deceit and control.

Gossip was never allowed in her home. At night, she would have me lay my head in her lap and tell me those ancient epic stories. I would always ask her what they meant. She would counsel me gently of the age-old truths of being true, kind, courageous and standing up for those who were less fortunate, reminding me that we are Spirit, and the more we were good, the more God's light would shine through our eyes and face.

She would tell me stories about the great Rama, who fought the evil Ravana, who had stolen Sita his beloved wife. Rama was bold and fought with honor, finally overcoming Ravana and bringing back his wife home to safety. That great epic of the *Ramayana*, the valiant journey of Rama, embedded in me a grand and uncompromising idealism for making the world a better place.

Living in Mumbai I was also exposed to the deplorable realities of India's caste system. My earliest memories, as a five-year-old, was realizing that we were "untouchables" --- low castes.

After playing soccer, I remember going to a nearby house with a friend to get some water. I was asked to stand outside, not allowed to enter, and given water in a markedly different kind of cup --- not the normal silverware. I later asked my mom what this meant. She said that we were low castes, and the home was that of an upper caste, and such segregation was how it was in India.

She shared with me how when she went to get water at the village well --- the upper caste would yell out to her as though she was a dirty animal and say, "shoo, shoo Shudra." The word "Shudra" is as derogatory and demeaning as the word "Nigger." She was only allowed to get water when they were not there.

So, as a child I wanted to understand not only the systems of ancient medicine my grandmother practiced to heal others but also the larger systems of oppression such as the caste system, and how to overcome and destroy it to bring truth, freedom and health to the world. Quite an ambition for a young child.

CHAPTER 2

The Invention of Email

It was these multiple worlds of Mumbai and
Muhavur that I was exposed to during my formative
years --- and it was that world I took with me when in
1970 my family emigrated from India to New Jersey, on
my seventh birthday.

My parents made this move for two reasons. First,
we were considered, as I shared, "untouchables" in the
Indian caste system, and, in spite of their incredible
capabilities and achievements as low-caste Indians, they
had hit a ceiling for advancement in India -- and
secondly, they wanted to find better educational
opportunities for their kids --- my sister and me.

However, 1970 was not a good year economically in
America. There was a recession underway and the
original job my father had been offered in Chicago didn't
work out as the recession had caused layoffs and job
reductions. So, we moved first to Paterson, New Jersey,

one of the poorest cities in the country, where my dad found an alternate job.

During my early years in New Jersey, I was certainly encouraged to do well in school, but I was also very much into sports. I wasn't the typical nerd. I was into baseball and soccer -- but I completed all the school's math courses, including Calculus, by the ninth grade, and even published a paper in a mathematics journal as a teenager. I did well in school for a very specific reason. I had been inspired by my grandmother and I wanted to learn medicine and healing. I had very practical goals.

At that time in 1977, the Courant Institute for Mathematical Science at NYU had started a new innovative program in which only forty young students were invited to come to NYU to study an intensive program in Computer Science --- an emerging field as computers themselves were very new.

This program was created by a visionary professor named Henry Mullish. He saw that software programming would one day be a primary need in the high tech revolution that was just beginning, and the United States would need software engineers. I was one of the forty students selected, and I learned eight programming languages at NYU. It was a twelve hour per day program and it went on for over two months. I was the only Indian in the program, and I was also the youngest student. I finished number one in the class.

Getting to NYU from New Jersey involved taking buses and trains, starting at around five in the morning. I'd arrive in New York around seven, and then walk to the University through the colorful and sometimes threatening environment that was New York in those days.

When the NYU program finished, I was very bored by the idea of going back to high school. I was even thinking about dropping out. Fortunately my mom had gotten a degree in statistics in India at a time when it was very unusual, or even revolutionary, for a woman to do anything like that. She was working as a systems analyst at a small, three-campus medical school called the University of Medicine and Dentistry of New Jersey (UMDNJ). Her job was located at the Newark campus of UMDNJ.

My mother introduced me to a scientist named Dr. Swamy Laxminarayan who had a large amount of data on the sudden crib death of infants in their sleep --- also known as SIDS. He asked me to explore the data using artificial intelligence and pattern analysis techniques to see if there was a correlation between infants' sleep patterns and crib death. I developed computer software algorithms to find such correlations. This was my introduction to AI and pattern analysis of what we today call "big data."

The results of my study were later published as a scientific paper at a major medical conference in Finland. This was very exciting and gratifying for me, since it was directly connected to my interest in medicine and healing. I was on my chosen path.

It turned out, however, that my ability to program the computer and work on sleep patterns had attracted the attention of another visionary scientist. His name was Dr. Leslie P. Michelson, and he was a brilliant PhD in experimental particle physics from Brookhaven Labs who was now at UMDNJ. Dr. Michelson had created the Laboratory Computer Network (LCN) which connected the three campuses of Newark, Piscataway and New Brunswick, in New Jersey. This network had nothing to do with the ARPANET or internet, etc. It was an independent network.

Dr. Michelson was also developing new scientific computing software applications to support research at UMDNJ. He had set high standards for any software that was created in his small computer lab at UMDNJ. It had to be bulletproof -- which meant it had to be highly reliable -- and it also had to be user friendly. I was only fourteen years old, but Dr. Michelson didn't treat me like a child. He wanted to challenge me. He wanted to push me as far as I could go.

Dr. Michelson told me about the interoffice mail system that was then used at UMDNJ, and was also used all over the country. He then challenged me to create software that would literally be an electronic replacement for the interoffice paper mail system that connected approximately one thousand offices at the three campuses of UMDNJ. The system I built included an Inbox, Outbox, Drafts, Folders, Memo, Attachments, Carbon Copies (including Blind Carbon Copies), Return Receipt, Address Book, Groups, Forward, Compose, Edit, Reply, Delete, Archive, Sort, and Bulk Distribution. I accomplished this task by writing nearly 50,000 lines of computer code across a system of 35 computer programs which I named "email" -- a term never before used in the English language. It was not a simple system, but a sophisticated enterprise class system.

It worked, was successful, and was used across the university. I wrote a user's manual, held user training sessions and maintained the system by fixing issues and adding new features --- all of this while finishing up some remaining courses in high school.

This whole experience was certainly a major turning point in my life. Creating a major invention like email was of course important. But even at the time I was aware that Dr. Michelson's giving me this assignment represented a complete and total rejection of any caste system -- yes, even in America -- based on age, race, or nationality. He opened the gates for me --- where a 14-year-old boy was invited to work alongside those who were three to five decades older, in a collegial environment, where I was treated no less, with the only expectation being that my work, the product of my labor, would be the judge of my stature --- nothing else.

This was freedom in the interests of science and innovation, and nothing else mattered. I wish I could say that everyone I've encountered in years since then has been as free from prejudice as Leslie Michelson, but that hasn't been the case. As a result, my work has often involved not only a search for innovation, but for justice as well.

At that time, in terms of electronic communication, earlier work had been done on sending rudimentary text messages between computers. But I want to emphasize that email was not just exchanging text messages. Email is a *system* with many interconnected parts that would enable collaboration in the electronic world as the interoffice mail system did in the world of paper and the physical world. Email was a full replica of the secretary's desktop along with all the communication features needed to transact business in an office environment.

Subsequently I won a Westinghouse Science Honors Award for creating email, and I was accepted at MIT. In fact, when I first arrived at MIT, the front page of the MIT newspaper featured three of the 1,041 incoming students' work, and I was one of them for having created email.

Email became something I had done in the past, I didn't focus on it, but I didn't entirely forget about it either. Upon attending MIT, in September of 1981, I learned from the MIT President Dr. Paul E. Gray during dinner at his home that the Supreme Court was not recognizing software patents; however, he advised me to Copyright my invention, since the recent Computer Software Act of 1980 allowed inventors to protect their software inventions using Copyright. That is what I did.

On August 30, 1982, the United States government awarded me the first U.S. Copyright for "Email." I want to emphasize this Copyright was significant since the Supreme Court was not yet recognizing software patents --- a Copyright was the only way to protect software inventions. Therefore, to the greatest extent possible at the time, I was officially recognized as the inventor of email by the United States government.

This sequence of events could have developed very differently if government policies regarding patents had not lagged behind the pace of innovation. Had I been allowed to patent email, I'd now be receiving a penny for every transmission and I'd be a gazillionaire.

CHAPTER 3

Somethings Need to Be Destroyed

Over the next thirty years I sought neither recognition nor financial gain for my invention of email. At MIT I earned four degrees in engineering and design, including a PhD in biological engineering. I was also interested in political systems, since I wanted answers to the oppressive caste system my family and I had experienced in India. I had the opportunity to study with Noam Chomsky, who is both the father of modern linguistics and also one of the most outspoken political thinkers in academia. I learned why and how the Indian caste system came into being --- a historical set of events that very few Indians are even aware of.

During my years at MIT, I always pursued entrepreneurial projects. I was in and out of the university, getting a degree, then leaving to start a company, then getting another degree --- one foot in academia, and one foot out.

By 1993, with the advent of the World Wide Web, email went from being a business application to becoming the dominant form of communication in all fields. At that time, I was doing my PhD in developing a universal AI and pattern analysis system for all sorts of media, including document content, handwriting analysis, and speech signals. During this time, the Clinton White House ran a competition to find an AI solution to their problem of email overload.

The White House had twenty interns sorting 5,000 emails a day into 147 predefined categories including education, healthcare, and many more. Each incoming email would be categorized into one of the categories, and then the sender would receive a form letter associated with a category. It was a very time consuming process. In an attempt to bring this situation under control, the government announced the competition for analyzing and sorting the emails. No such thing had ever been done before, because there had been no need for anything like this.

I entered the competition as the only graduate student. The other entrants were five public and private companies. I won and was selected to provide the service.

Out of that experience I started a company called EchoMail, which helped major corporations process large volumes of email from clients and customers. I thought EchoMail would be a two year project. However, it became a ten year enterprise with 300 employees, and I grew it to $250 million in value. I personally made a lot of money.

In the midst of this, in 2003, my advisor called and urged me come back to MIT to finish my PhD. A major global science initiative, called the Human Genome Project, had just ended which mapped the entire human genome. Despite what the scientists had expected, it turned out that human beings have approximately the same number of genes as an earthworm --- about 20,000. In this atmosphere, the field of *systems biology* was coming into its own, saying we needed to look beyond genes as the "answer to everything." We needed to see the interconnections of molecules across the genome and their communication in cells, just as my grandmother had seen how the facial features of someone connected to their bodily functions.

At this time the National Science Foundation (NSF) had issued what they called the "Grand Challenge," comparable to landing on the moon. The challenge was to mathematically model the whole human cell. I returned to MIT and combined my love of computers with my devotion to medicine and created the technology of CytoSolve in response to the NSF challenge. If Email was the electronic version of the interoffice mail communication system, CytoSolve was the electronic version of the molecular communication system. This could mean the final elimination of animal testing in laboratories.

Based on my work on CytoSolve, MIT awarded me a PhD. In that same year in 2007 I received a Fulbright Fellowship to return to India to study Siddha from a systems biology perspective. The front page of MIT's official newspaper, *MIT Tech Talk*, headlined a feature article: "East meets West: Armed with 4 MIT degrees, Shiva Ayyadurai embarks on new adventure."

This had been my childhood aspiration to understand scientifically how my grandmother was able to heal others using Siddha. My training in systems biology at MIT provided me all the necessary skills.

I discovered that the Siddhars had always been systems thinkers. Unlike conventional Western medicine, they were not reductionist. They didn't look at people and their health in a fragmented way. Their view of health was genuinely holistic.

I discovered a common language, a science, that connected Siddha with modern control systems theory. This was a major breakthrough, and would become the basis of my future teaching and curriculum on Systems Health and "The Science of Everything."

On the night before I was set to leave India to return to the US, following completion of my Fulbright research in 2009, I was called to a meeting with the Director General of the Council of Scientific and Industrial Research (CSIR). CSIR was India's largest scientific enterprise comprised of 37 labs across India and over 4,500 scientists. He invited me to serve as the head of the CSIR's new initiative, "CSIR-TECH," to spin out scientific innovations -- innovations that had just been sitting in the lab -- to the general population of India. The idea was to expedite the transition from the lab bench to the masses.

In this role, I developed a strategic plan for unleashing innovation from those labs by implementing an entrepreneurial program. I visited nearly 1,500 CSIR

Indian scientists all over the country and met people who were absolutely brilliant. Amazing innovations were being developed. But these innovations were being sidetracked by administrators and bureaucrats who were jealous and afraid. There was a high level of corruption.

I wrote an honest report in October of 2009 that exposed the sycophancy, corruption and suppression that was taking place in Indian science. Within hours, I was fired, and was later evicted from my home. Death threats followed, and also threats from the Director General to reporters of major papers: they were not to share the facts. I was forced to flee India on a dramatic journey that included a 32-hour train ride to the Nepal border, plane flight to Kathmandu, and three other airplane flights before I was finally back home in Boston.

Prior to my dismissal, I had been awarded the First Outstanding Scientist/Technologist of Indian Origin by the Prime Minister of India, who serves as the President of CSIR. I had been appointed as Additional Secretary in the Indian government, with the highest Scientist Level H posting. Major newspapers, including *The New York Times*, covered the events of my dismissal, in spite of threats from the Director General of CSIR against NY Times reporters. I was commissioned to write an article for *Nature* by the Nature India editor, which I entitled "Innovation Demands Freedom." Shortly after this article was published, the editor of Nature India was threatened by the then Prime Minister's Office, and the article was removed.

Sometime after I returned to Boston, in late 2011, my mother was dying of pulmonary fibrosis. Much to my surprise, she presented me with a suitcase filled with all the artifacts of my early work on email from 1978 -- my fifty thousand lines of code, everything.

One of my colleagues, a professor at Emerson College reviewed the materials and said, "Shiva, you invented email." As I reviewed the materials, I could, however, only think back to the amazing collegial ecosystem at UMDNJ which allowed a 14-year-old boy to innovate and invent email --- far different than the oppressive and draconian feudal system of CSIR in India, which suppressed innovation.

My friend contacted Doug Aamoth, who was the Technology Editor at *Time Magazine*. Doug reviewed the materials carefully over many weeks and wrote a feature article entitled "The Man Who Invented Email," which informed the general public about email's true origin. In 2012, the Smithsonian Institution's National Museum of American History (NMAH) requested and received the artifacts that documented my work, which really did epitomize the American Dream.

On February 16, 2012, an event was held at the Smithsonian to celebrate the acquisition of all that material. It was after that ceremony that controversy began, which is extensively documented on the Internet. The "controversy" was incited by a group calling itself a "special interest group" body of "computer historians" --- these were industry insiders, loyal to the major defense contractor Raytheon/BBN, who had falsely crowned one of its own employees as the "inventor of email."

After three decades of not promoting my work, these people attacked me as if I were a money-hungry opportunist. The online gossip site Gizmodo called me an "asshole," "a dick," and "a fraud." These inspired threats on other blogs that "the curry-stained Indian should be shot and hanged by his dhothi," and expletives such as "nigger Indian."

Why were there such vicious attacks against me? The reason is simple. The idea that a 14-year-old immigrant Indian boy working in an obscure hospital could invent email disrupted the carefully nurtured storyline that major innovations always had to come from the triangle of big corporations, major universities and the military --- what President Eisenhower and Senator Fulbright had referred to as the "military-industrial-academic" complex.

Specifically, concerning email, those innovations had to come from defense contractors. Therefore those defense contractors should receive whatever huge funding they wanted, because so many wonderful things like email came out of that -- which in actuality had not come from military initiatives.

But the facts on who invented email are black and white. There never was a genuine controversy. The whole media storm was fabricated to continue brainwashing Americans with the idea that innovations come from war, and we as Americans should be happy funding war since we get Tang and Velcro --- which by the way also didn't come from military research either.

The attacks on my reputation were libelous and defamatory. However, I was not able to find an attorney to take on this Goliath of an enemy.

In 2016, after four years of attempting to find an attorney, I signed with Charles Harder, who represented the ex-pro wrestler Hulk Hogan in a highly publicized case against Gawker Media. Charles Harder filed a suit against Gawker Media and I was victorious.

On November 3, 2016 Gawker Media settled with me for $750,000 and removed all three defamatory online articles. This was a big victory for the inventor of email, and more importantly it established the truth that innovation, small or large, can occur anytime, anyplace, by anybody.

Immediately after this victory, the response from the defeated cabal of vested interests was exactly what would be expected: a desire for revenge. This was expressed by frantic blog posts stating that "Shiva Ayyadurai didn't invent email."

Their belief seemed to be that, if they said it loud enough, that untruth would become fact. This is a familiar tactic of those in power: repeat a lie loud and long in order to brainwash the masses.

As this false storyline was being created, the establishment cabal then colluded together to further libel and defame me on the very influential Wikipedia site. Within weeks of my legal victory, the cabal rewrote the opening sentences of my Wikipedia page, -- which would be the first item on a Google search -- stating that the only notable achievement of my life was to have created a controversy by asserting myself as the inventor of email.

But in fact there was no longer any controversy, if there ever had been one. The fact is that I had won and that win would be recognized by a payment of $750,000 from the people who had libeled me in contradiction of the facts.

The defamatory articles were removed because the business folks at Gawker Media and Univision did not want to suffer even greater damage to their wallets. Money, in an odd way, can sometimes motivate justice.

My experiences have brought renewed knowledge of how systems work, and that knowledge will be most powerful weapon to destroy whatever systems oppress the broad mass of humanity. At that same time, that knowledge will provide the insight to create and embrace systems that bring us truth, freedom and health --- as did the Siddha system that my grandmother practiced, without any college degrees.

My core mission, in this book and everywhere else, is to bring you an understanding of systems theory and practice. With that understanding, you will see for yourself that truth is an emergent property arising from the interconnections of the components of any system.

Email, therefore, is not a simple exchange of text messages, but a system which emerges from the interconnection of the many components originally resident in the interoffice mail system. Health emerges from complex, dynamic combinations biological elements -- not from one "magic bullet" drug, or diet, or exercise.

In a similar way, real freedom will not emerge from fighting one aspect of the enemy, whether it's racism, sexism, or classism. Freedom will come from defeating the priesthood system of academia, media, politics, and even entertainment that keeps humanity in bondage through a complex interaction of oppression. The ultimate goal of that system is to dehumanize the many by asserting that only the few are innovative, intelligent, beautiful, and all-knowing.

For the great Siddhars, the revolutionaries, the warriors, the heart of their struggle was against these priesthoods and their caste system. Some things do need to be destroyed --- and that caste system is one such thing.

PART 2

Systems Biology

CHAPTER 4

Revolutionary Road

When I enrolled at MIT as a first year student I was of course very oriented toward science, but I also was more socially engaged than many of my classmates. A pair of photographs from MIT expresses these diverging interests. In one, the school's official student newspaper, *The Tech*, had a front page article featuring achievements of three of the 1,041 incoming students. I was one of the three, and my invention of email was highlighted.

A more dramatic photo in several issues later shows me as a 17-year-old undergraduate burning a South African flag on the steps of the MIT Student Center. I had just led a major protest of several thousand students and workers against MIT's investments in apartheid South Africa. I later challenged the MIT administration to provide proper wages for food service workers and increased student enrollment of women, minorities, and those of lower socio-economic background. On the date of my PhD graduation, as I was receiving my degree, I pulled out a big sign, which said "U.S. Out of Iraq." Half the crowd booed me, and the other half cheered.

I was inspired to act on my own, and to organize the local community against inequities, whether thousands of miles away or right at home. That inspiration was fueled by my personal desire to understand and change *systems* --- systems of oppression like the Indian caste system.

My path as a student at MIT, along with my experiences in India, would be the basis for my future work in the new field of Systems Biology --- as this field provided a much needed opportunity for a systems-based approach to biology.

To get started in understanding Systems Biology, let's look at those two words individually. A system is any set of connecting things, working together with a specific goal or purpose. We are all familiar with mechanical systems: Your car is a system; so is your cell phone. Some systems are relatively simple; others are more complicated, containing within them a variety of still other systems.

The house or apartment in which you live is one example; think about the systems it holds, such as electrical, plumbing, and heating. Look around and what do you see? Do you have a washing machine, a dishwasher, a computer, a CD player, a clock, a pencil sharpener, or iPhone? These are all systems.

What about the word "biology"? Biology is the study of all living things. In modern biology, we study life by conducting simple and complex experiments. In biology, as yet there are no mathematical laws, and there may never be. There are no equations available to predict how tall someone will become under various circumstances based on how much food this person eats or what kind of sports he plays. This is different from physics where observations and many experiments have created mathematical laws that always hold true. Biology, therefore, is fundamentally an experimental science and experiments are the key to the knowledge we have thus far acquired.

Systems Biology is a way of applying the science of systems to the study of life, in all its forms. The mission of systems biology is to give us a new way to grasp the complexity of life. It requires integration of multiple disciplines. In recent years nearly every major university has formed a department called Systems Biology. These are actually interdisciplinary departments bringing together scientists, engineers, and designers across the disciplines of engineering, science and the arts. The complexity of Systems Biology requires this level of cooperative research.

One of the most far-reaching applications of systems biology is Personalized Medicine or Precision Medicine. With my continuing interest in medicine that began with my grandmother, Personalized Medicine was one of the things that attracted me to Systems Biology. Personalized Medicine means that one day you will be able to go to your doctor's office (or possibly simply get on the internet) to access your DNA, which has already been stored in a secure information repository, and submit a sample of that day's blood or saliva. Within moments you will get a read out telling you exactly what to eat for that day and what activities you should do to optimize your day's health.

This is revolutionary change, since most medicine is currently based on a "one size fits all." Pharmaceutical companies spend years finding one drug to cure a particular disease across all people. And the poor results are demonstrating year after year that one drug does not work for everyone. In fact, most drugs work effectively for no more than 10% of the population.

Some patients have an immediate positive response to a drug; others have a variety of side effects. A specific drug may not work for certain people, who are subject to certain conditions. Systems biology hopes to cure this fundamental problem. With a molecular understanding of each one of us as individual and unique beings, it will help deliver the right medicine, at the right time, for the right person.

However, we cannot even think about getting there, until we recognize that *reductionism* is the barrier that needs to be overcome to achieve the grand vision of systems biology.

CHAPTER 5

Beyond Reductionism

Since 1687, when Sir Isaac Newton first published his famous work, *Philosophiae Naturalis Principia*, modern science has been based on a simple and reasonably reliable assumption: If you want to understand anything, you need to take it apart. Many of us remember taking that first biology course in high school or middle school.

We most likely began our study of trees by looking at leaves. This has been the accepted approach to all scientific and mechanical problems: Want to understand a watch, take it apart and examine the pieces. Want to figure out why an engine runs? Examine the pieces. Want to figure out how a human being functions? Look at the parts one at a time. In a Newtonian world, if you understand the parts, you can understand the whole. It's certainly easy to understand why this approach can be so appealing. Some things are simply too complex and huge to grasp any other way. It's complicated so we reduce it down to its parts. This approach is known as *reductionism*.

Reductionism has contributed greatly to human knowledge, but it has its limitations. It's easy to see these limitations in medicine when our bodies are approached as though they are broken up, as it were, into a group of organs and limbs, specialties and sub-specialties. A friend of mine recently visited her internist with a sinus infection. The internist sent her to an ear, nose, throat specialist. The ENT examined her and made some recommendations for medication. My friend complained that a post-nasal drip making its way from the sinuses through her throat and into her lungs was giving her a bad cough. The ENT said he was sorry but the cough involved the lungs, and he didn't treat anything below the neck.

As medical consumers, we know how exasperating this can be. We know that we can't always divide our bodies up into parts. We know that the foot bone is connected to the ankle bone and the ankle bone is connected to the shin bone and the shin bone is connected to the knee bone. Yet, if we have a foot pain <u>and</u> a knee pain, we have to visit at least two different doctors, who in all probability are not consulting with each other to determine if there is a connection. This is one of the problems associated with a reductionist approach to health.

Modern science is beginning to realize that a reductionist approach gives only part of the entire picture—only a portion of the truth. When you connect a bunch of things, whether they are auto parts or human parts, something emerges that is greater and different than the sum of its parts. Take something as basic as a clock. If you take a clock apart, it's nothing more than a collection of odd assorted pieces. When it's put together in the right order, with the right connections, a clock assumes an almost magical function in terms of what it does and how a reliance on an accurate reading of time impacts your world. If this is true for a clock, imagine what happens when you are talking about a living organism, whether it is a tree, an animal, or a human being.

Systems theory is a direct pushback against reductionism, particularly with regard to health and wellness. Proponents of systems theory quote Aristotle who clearly stated, "The whole is different from the sum of its parts." A systems approach to health takes the human spirit as well as the mind-body connection into account. Men and women who want to take a more holistic approach to health frequently engage in practices like meditation and yoga; they are more careful about what they eat and look for ways to encourage spiritual as well as physical healing. Modern New Age movements have popularized holistic health practices. And to the shock and often annoyance of some of the medical establishment, these methods sometimes work.

Those who like to point out the failures of so-called "alternative" techniques tend to focus on the word "sometimes." This is a valid criticism. Practitioners of holistic healing can't always satisfactorily duplicate their results. They can't explain successes using the rigors of modern science, which requires standardization and reproducibility; when something works, they can't explain why. Instead of scientific explanations, what we see and hear is a fair amount of hand waving and conversations using buzzwords like "meridians," "detox," and "energy." New Age healing extremists often go too far and throw science completely out the window. This approach encourages people to avoid modern medicine altogether and rely instead on peculiar diets, questionable herbal methods, and unreliable faith healers.

Here's the problem: when the complex system that is your body has a complex illness, a reductionist approach may not give you the healing you need; similarly a new holistic diet combined with meditation or any other alternative method will have its own limitations.

Complex problems require solutions that speak to the big picture, which is where a systems approach is most helpful. A systems-based approach to life may help us find the middle way between reductionism and holism. It helps us understand the whole as an interconnection of parts, not just the sum of its parts. It helps us recognize the values as well as the weaknesses in a Newtonian world model, which implies that there is always a certain linear cause and effect predictability.

CHAPTER 6

Systems of Systems

A systems-based approach to biology emerges where reductionism ends. Reductionist thinking and the central dogma of Watson and Crick had emphasized that genes alone make us who we are. However, this has proven to be completely wrong.

Since biology is the primary source of knowledge and insight for developing healthcare treatments, the necessary and significant changes to advance modern healthcare, therefore, cannot take place without changes in how biology itself is practiced. Biology today, unlike physics or engineering, is based on experiments rather than first principles, *ab initio*. Biologists do many experiments to understand genes, proteins, and protein-protein interactions.

The all-time largest and most ambitious experiment in biology was the Human Genome Project (HGP,) begun in 1990 and completed around 2003.

The HGP was predicated on the hypothesis that what made a human different from a nematode, a worm, was the number of genes. Originally, it was estimated that a human had approximately 100,000 genes. But the HGP concluded that humans have only 20,000 to 25,000 genes, far less than what was originally theorized. This was almost the same number of genes as the 19,000 genes possessed by the nematode *Caenorhabditis elegans*. The genome of the starlet sea anemone *Nematostella vectensis*, a delicate animal only a few inches long, has approximately 18,000 genes.

Regardless of whether human or nematodes or sea anemone have similar numbers of genes, the HGP revealed great differences in their complexity of function as whole organisms. This apparent contradiction led biologists to conclude that perhaps the number of genes in the genome is not directly connected an organism's complexity. Instead, much of that complexity can be ascribed to regulation of existing genes by other substances (such as proteins) rather than to novel genes. Molecular interactions across the nucleus, cytoplasm, and organelles -- beyond the number of genes in the nucleus itself -- may be a critical element in determining the difference between a human and a worm.

This reasoning has led to an even greater determination to understand the structure of proteins (e.g. the product of genes) and protein–protein interactions. In short, the HGP demonstrated that we are not our genes --- that who we are is likely something that emerges from the complex interplay of genes and the products of genes interacting in ways where genes can be turned on and off.

These results mean that we need to move to *systems* biology that focuses attention not only on the genome, but on the complex interaction of "systems of systems" across genes, proteins, and molecular pathways. All these are influenced by an "epigenetic" layer affected by both endogenous and exogenous systems including nutrition, environment, and perhaps even thoughts that affect genes themselves.

This system of systems approach aims to create a holistic model of the whole organism by integrating the complexity of systems of systems from molecule, to molecular pathways, to large-scale organization, as illustrated below:

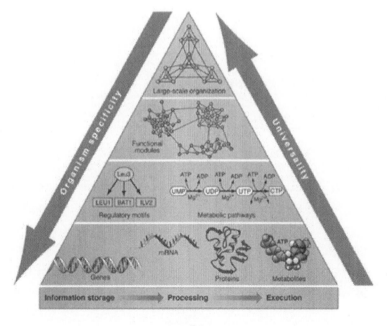

An important attribute of the complexity pyramid is the gradual transition from the particular (at the bottom level) to the universal (at the top.) Integrated models can represent the most compact, unambiguous, and unified form of biological hypotheses, and as such they could be used to quantitatively explore interrelationships at both the molecular and cellular levels.

Although systems biology is a new field, building a systems-level understanding of biology is not a new phenomenon. More than 5,000 years ago, traditional systems of medicine including Siddha, Unani, Ayurveda, and Traditional Chinese Medicine (TCM) proposed systems approaches to describe the whole human physiome. In modern times, starting in 1930s with the concept of homeostasis and biological cybernetics, attempts were made to understand biology at a systems level using the languages of physics and control systems engineering.

Systems biology is now developing a systems-level understanding by connecting our knowledge of activity at the molecular level to higher-level biological functions. Previous attempts at system-level approaches were primarily limited to description and analysis of biological systems at the physiological level. Since these approaches had little understanding of how molecular interactions were linked to biological functions, a systems-based biology that connected molecular interactions to biological functions was not possible.

Contemporary systems biology, however, offers a new opportunity to link the behaviors of molecules to the characteristics of biological systems. This new field will enable us to describe the systems of systems of cells, tissues, organs, and human beings within a consistent framework governed by the basic principles of physics.

CHAPTER 7

Modeling the Whole Cell

In 2003, after having been the CEO of EchoMail, Inc. for nearly 10 years, my advisor Prof. C. Forbes Dewey asked me to come back to MIT to complete my Ph.D. At that time, as I shared earlier, the Human Genome Project had just ended with the ironic conclusion that humans have about 20,000 genes --- the same number as an earthworm. Not only did this discovery lead to the field of systems biology but also to another development.

This development was the impetus to mathematically model the whole cell. The National Science Foundation (NSF) had put forward this "Grand Challenge" to inspire scientists to create a computer model of the cell. This challenge intrigued me as it provided a unique opportunity to express my love of computing and medicine.

The systems approach here was to consider the cell as a system of interconnected molecular pathways, which were the elemental modules of complex cellular functions. Biological systems were thought to have large number of parts which are related in complex ways. Functionality, therefore, emerges as the result of molecular interactions between many proteins relating to each other in multiple cascades and in interaction with the cellular environment.

Computing these molecular interactions could determine the logic of healthy and diseased states. One way to model the whole cell would be through a "bottom up" reconstruction of the human metabolic network, which was done primarily through a manual process of integrating databases and pathway models.

It was possible to regard molecular networks as systems that decode and transform complex inputs in time, space, and chemistry into combinatorial output patterns of signaling activity. In this way, accurate experimentation and detailed modeling of network behavior in terms of molecular properties could reinforce each other. The goal then becomes a linking of molecular pathway models on small parts to build larger models in order to form detailed kinetic models of larger chunks of molecular pathways, such as metabolism, for example, and ultimately of the entire living cell.

Integrating systems of molecular pathways demonstrates how integrated networks show emergent properties that the individual pathways do not possess -- including extended signal duration, activation of feedback loops, thresholds for biological effects, or a multitude of signal outputs. In this sense, a cell can be seen as an adaptive autonomous agent or as a society of such agents, where each can exhibit a particular behavior depending on its cognitive capabilities.

Unique mathematical frameworks would be needed to obtain an integrated perspective on these complex systems, which operate over wide length and time scales. These may involve multi-layered, hierarchical approaches, in which the overall signaling network at one layer is modeled in terms of effective "circuit" or "algorithm" modules. Then, at other layers, each module is correspondingly modeled with more detailed incorporation of its actual underlying biochemical and biophysical molecular interactions.

The mammalian cell may be considered as a central signaling network connected to various cellular machines that are responsible for phenotypic functions. Cellular machines such as transcriptional, translational, motility, and secretory machinery can be represented as sets of interacting components that form functional local networks.

As biology began to move into the post-genomic era, a key emerging question concerns the understanding of complex molecular pathways functioning as dynamical systems. Prominent examples include multi-molecular protein "machines," intracellular signal transduction cascades, and cell–cell communication mechanisms. As the proportion of identified systems involved in any of these molecular pathways continues to increase, the daunting challenge of developing useful models – both mathematical and conceptual - for how they work was drawing increased interest.

Multi-scale modeling, I realized, would be essential to integrating knowledge of human physiology -- starting with genomics, molecular biology, and the environment through the levels of cells, tissues, and organs -- all the way to integrated systems behavior. The lowest levels concern biophysical and biochemical events. The higher levels of organization in tissues, organs, and organism are complex, representing the dynamically varying behavior of billions of cells interacting together.

Biological pathways can be seen to share structural principles with engineered networks, along with three of the most important shared principles: modularity, robustness to component tolerances, and use of recurring circuit elements.

These insights led me, as a part of my MIT Ph.D. research, to create CytoSolve --- "Cyto" meaning cell and "Solve" meaning solving. CytoSolve was created to be new computer-based platform for integrating systems of biological pathway models. I also refer to it as a "collaboratory" --- meaning the different engineering components of the cell could be organized, modeled and then integrated together through collaboration.

CytoSolve is a system that enables computational collaboration and integration --- not that different than email. If email is the system that was the electronic replica of the mail communication system, then CytoSolve is the electronic replica of the molecular communication system. More importantly, just as email was a revolution in communication, CytoSolve is a revolution in medicine.

Within 11 months, for example, CytoSolve was used to discover a combination therapy of drugs that was shown to perform *in silico* (on the computer) better than the current "gold standard" for pancreatic cancer. Our combination received FDA allowance to proceed to clinical trials within that 11 months. The possibilities of CytoSolve's applications for medicine and health are limitless.

PART 3

The First Systems Biology

CHAPTER 8

Siddha and Ayurveda

After completing my Ph.D. in systems biology in 2007, I wanted to take some time off from academia to go back to the field and pursue my childhood dream to understand how my grandmother was able to heal those villagers. How did Siddha, that ancient system of Indian medicine, work? I felt that my training at MIT provided me a solid foundation in both Western biology as well as in engineering. This foundation could be used to apply a rigorous scientific and critical approach in understanding Siddha. Funding from the Fulbright Fellowship provided me the opportunity to pursue this research, entitled "Siddha to Systems Biology."

A detailed review of Siddha (and Ayurveda as it is known in Northern parts of India) will provide a framework for you to appreciate the journey to the Science of Everything. Siddha and Ayurveda are ancient systems of Indian medicine that have been practiced for over 5,000 years.

Siddha is from the Tamil word meaning "perfection." Ayurveda means "knowledge of life," from the words "ayus" (life) and "veda" (knowledge.) Siddha is predominantly practiced in southern India, while Ayurveda is mainly practiced in the north. Siddha and Ayurveda have particular differences, such as emphasis on particular modalities and minor variations in terminology, but their foundational elements are the same.

We in the West tend to think that the scientific system that has been built here is the only legitimate one. This is not true. Scientific methods have been used for thousands of years in places Westerners do not normally think of as having anything in common with American or European colleges and universities.

When I came to MIT as a first year student, I remember walking onto 77 Massachusetts Avenue and standing on the steps of the domed building; I immediately noticed how much it resembled the temples I knew in India. Thousands of years ago, before what we now call the Common Era, Siddha teachers, who occupied those temples and used nature as their laboratory, developed disciplined scientific methods and approaches.

These Siddhars, or "Rishis," were scientists, no different than a modern research scholar or professor. They conducted detailed research, experimented, taught, took on students and published through song and poetry. They developed an understanding of nature that recognized the individuality of each of human being, and found ways to link that individuality to the interconnected system of nature around them. They solved problems that we are only now beginning to investigate, so it behooves us to take them seriously.

As I've mentioned earlier, my interest in medicine and my knowledge of the Siddhars began by observing my grandmother, Chinnathai. One truth that my grandmother shared with me, at an early age, was The Law of Karma: "For every cause there is an effect." When my grandmother said these words, she was reminding me that everything in life is interconnected. Drop a pebble into a stream, and it sets off a series of consequences; ripples have meaning.

Ancient sages also referenced these words, which for millennia were seen as merely a poetic or spiritual statement of the concept of Karma, and, unfortunately, sometimes used to rationalize oppression and one's lot in life. However when Isaac Newton echoed a similar allegory, "For every action there is an equal and opposite reaction" and demonstrated the reality of these words through modern science, the words took on a material reality, beyond religious obfuscations, and changed the course of modern history.

Newton demonstrated how physical bodies interact and predicted the motion of these interactions with precision. His discovery, known as Newton's Law of Motion, unleashed the creation of modern science and society. The reality he unraveled created modern machines, bridges, airplanes, cars, skyscrapers, and spaceships that landed on the moon. Newton's insights and experiments gave concrete meaning to the spiritual concept of Karma.

I learned about Karma as a child in India. Here in America, when I learned about Newton's Law of Motion, I couldn't help but relate it back to my grandmother's words. It seemed fairly apparent to me that Newton and the Indian sages my grandmother so often referenced were saying the same thing. Both Newton and the Siddhars were wise men who came to their conclusions using their powers of observation. Newton arrived at his conclusions through the power of observation, which he wrote down as math equations.

But there was no available mathematical language for Newton to use so he developed his own—calculus. When we think of the original Siddha elders, we don't think of them as scientists. Yet, they were. Like Newton, they were using the oldest scientific methods of observation; their university was all of nature. Siddha practitioners observed the body. They watched breath, listened to heartbeats, recognized the importance of thoughts and intentions. Their wisdom is all arrived at through observation.

I was constantly amazed by what my grandmother knew just from looking at a person's face. Her powers of observation, without the help of any instruments, were incredible. She saw colorings, marks, moles, lines, locations and asymmetries. Her mind and training connected these features to areas of imbalance in the body.

After determining the issues, she would then prescribe a treatment. Sometimes, she suggested the taking of an appropriate herb; other times she prescribed the repetition of certain sounds or mantras; when necessary, she performed a body manipulation. These treatments were aimed at correcting the imbalances she diagnosed from the face. It sounds amazing, but my grandmother was able to diagnose someone's problem simply by observing his or her face. She was able to prescribe treatments that worked.

My grandmother's skills at face reading and her medical treatments were based on Siddha methods and teachings. The 5,000 year old Siddha medical system is one of the oldest in the world, and the oldest still practiced. Siddha medicine is an Indian system developed in the Southern Indian region of Tamil. The word Siddha means "fully perfected" or "enlightened." Most of us have heard the name "Siddhartha" or "enlightened one" used in reference to the Buddha who lived some 2,500 years ago.

The ancient teachings say the Siddha system was directly transmitted by Lord Shiva to his wife Parvathi. Parvathi then gave the knowledge to one of her two sons, Muruga. Muruga, a Hindu deity, then transmitted it to Agastya, a sage, who is known as the father of Siddha medicine. Agastya, in turn, passed these teachings and knowledge on to seventeen other Siddhars.

These eighteen highly evolved beings, regarded as spiritual saints, then established a lineage of information and wisdom that has come down to us over the centuries. The Siddha scriptures are practical as well as esoteric and contain teachings on all aspects of life including science, meditation, yogi, alchemy, tantra, medicine, art, enlightenment, and herbal treatments.

People often wonder how all this could have been transmitted in such complete form for so many years. In ancient India, the Siddha scriptures were preserved by scribes who carefully etched Siddha wisdom, including medical formularies, onto treated palm leaves. The etched lettering was then treated with dyes made from coal black or turmeric. These palm leaves formed collections of manuscripts that could last for centuries. When these treasured manuscripts started to deteriorate, new scribes went to work, using the same methods. Thousands and thousands of palm leaf manuscripts have been passed down in this way. Currently, scholars and specialists have started work collecting, transcribing, and cataloguing what has been found.

Many of the texts saved in this way focus on the use of herbal medicinal formularies, face reading, sound, crystals, as well as different types of yoga, visualization, and meditation. There were even texts devoted to art and drawing—what we would now call art therapy. In India, the Siddha medical system continues to be practiced today, and you can still get a Siddha MD degree. Siddhars are also renowned as artists and poets, and much of the teachings handed down through time are in the form of songs and poetry. It's interesting to note that in these ancient teachings, medicine is viewed as both science and art.

CHAPTER 9

Layers of Meaning

The texts of Siddha were written in poetic form which could be recited as a poem or a song. Each poem had two meanings. There was the apparent or face value meaning of the poem, and then there was the medical or more esoteric meaning, which revealed a higher truth.

The apparent meaning enabled lay people to enjoy the poem as a work of art. The more esoteric meaning could only be deciphered by those who were either their disciples or had the acumen and intuition to see beyond the visible meaning. In some sense, the Siddhars presented even their knowledge in visible and invisible forms, requiring one to perceive the invisible and understand it, to reveal the real meaning and truth behind the verse.

Consider the following example of a simple poem, which is written in Tamil as follows:

Mangai paal vundu
Malaimai irruporkuu

Thengai paal
Eythikkadi kuthambai

Here's an English translation:
>Those drinking mango milk
>And living on a hill
>Coconut milk,
>Is not needed

At face value, this poem relates the power of mango milk. For anyone who has seen a mango on a tree, will notice a small amount of white milk, like sap, comes from the stem when the mango is plucked. This milk is normally ignored and seen as nothing significant having no value. The poem states that this seemingly insignificant milk has a powerful nutritional value to those living on a hill; and this value, is even more potent than the highly nutritious and valued coconut milk.

But a Siddhar disciple would, however, decipher the poem, beyond that apparent and literal meaning, as follows: The hill represents the top of the head --- the "hill" of the human body. The mango is the pineal gland, located between the two eyebrows on top of the head. The mango milk is the hormone, melatonin, however small the amount, the pineal gland secretes through the right meditative practices. According to the Siddhars, this "milk" is an elixir, far healthier than any food in the world, including coconut milk, which the Siddhars considered one of the most nutritious foods.

Siddhars codified their knowledge in poetic verses with dual meanings to ensure that the truths were made accessible to those who had the right training. They recognized the immense power of their teachings, acquired over many millennia of scientific observation and experimentation, and wanted to protect them from those who could misuse it or did not have the relevant training to use it appropriately. Over the many centuries, Siddhars have continued to take this approach, passing it on to only their most trusted followers.

The Indo-Aryan invasions resulted in much of the Siddhars' knowledge being suppressed; some of it was incorporated into Vedic texts, such as Ayurveda, which many in the West are more aware of. Furthermore, the British invasion resulted in the suppression of many of the Indian traditional practices in favor of western medicine. Today, unlike my grandmother, the average Indian interested in medicine are taught that traditional systems of medicine such as Siddha are inferior to Western medicine.

Fortunately in 2005 after much lobbying by those who were interested in bringing Siddha to the modern world, the government of India inaugurated the National Institute of Siddha, in the southern state of Tamil Nadu. This Institute today is focused on converting the hundreds of thousands of the ancient Siddha texts written in Tamil poetry. Over the next few years, more and more knowledge of the Siddhars art and medicine will be made available.

Hundreds of thousands of palm leaves are filled with this kind of artistic poetry which reveal both an apparent concept and a more hidden and valuable truth. The original teachings of Siddha stressed enlightenment or spiritual perfection, but it's important to note that Siddhars taught that enlightenment and physical health are intrinsically linked. They believed that methods that strengthened one's physical well being would lead to greater spiritual growth. To this end, they developed practices emphasizing diet, yoga, and meditation that would help practitioners become healthier as they sought to become Siddhars or "perfected ones."

My grandmother told me that Siddhars believed that the entire cosmos, from the smallest particle to the largest solar systems, were connected by consciousness and energy. Siddha practitioners taught, "As above, so below." If you want to understand natural law, start by observing the dynamics of your own body. Understand yourself, and you will understand the whole world.

Over thousands of years, the Siddhars developed and organized a holistic system of understanding based on observable patterns of interaction. Here in the West, Systems biology is building an understanding of the universe bottom-up from cell to tissue to organs to intact organism.

Siddha, on the other hand, understands the world top-down as energy permeating from the cosmos to the ecosystem, to human, to organs to tissue. As I continued my study of Siddha medicine and Systems Biology, I came to recognize the potential of integrating Siddha and Systems Biology to build a convergent understanding of life, integrating the top-down and bottom up approaches of ancient and modern medicine.

CHAPTER 10

Siddha's Model of a Human Being

The Siddhars taught that there is a temple within each of us. But what exactly does that mean? Is this a spiritual concept? And where exactly is this temple located? How do we find it?

The concept of a "temple within" is <u>not based</u> on mysticism. The ancient Siddhars were considered radicals because they opposed many of the mystical religious traditions then prevalent in India. They were focused on the quest for Truth and that state of perfection, known as Siddhi. They were against codified scriptures, superstition, blind devotion, and guru worship. Although they were not atheistic or agnostic, they had no real concept of deities as we think of them now. They considered themselves scientists, not mystics.

In the Siddha tradition, everything is related to science: it all started with unmanifest energy, which they called Purusha or consciousness. When consciousness awakens, energy appears and interacts; and then Nature unfolds from energy to matter, through various levels. Siddha is about understanding not only the body but also the nature of all things that interact with the body including the larger systems from the microscopic to the macroscopic. But Siddha concepts concerning the human body and the physical nature of man are quite different from what we learn here in the West.

The Siddhars as scientists developed their precise model of a person based on their experiments and observations. They came to the fundamental conclusion that the human body possessed a complete infrastructure to find truth at all levels of existence.

This thesis is different from the Western view of the human being. Siddha research led to an important conclusion, one as real as gravity: each one of us is made up of three separate and interconnected systems: The Visible Body; The Invisible Body; and the Atman, the infinite and unknowable.

Western medicine is primarily concerned with the physical or visible body. Siddhars said that if we want to understand the puzzle that is man, we need to take all three systems into account. If we fail to do this, we are not seeing the whole picture.

An important point to remember: Siddhars taught that both the visible self and the invisible self were part of the manifest material world. In short, both the seen and the unseen human systems are described as a continuum between matter and energy --- the visible self having more matter and the invisible self being composed of more energy. They acknowledged that some things are not visible to the human eye but that doesn't make them any less real and tangible. Here, again, are the three systems that make up the individual man or woman.

The Visible Self -- Discussions of the Visible Self include all the parts of self that can be heard, felt, smelled, seen or touched.

The Invisible Self -- Discussions of the invisible self include our emotional and spiritual selves; they include our five senses, as well as our various states of mind, including the conscious state, subconscious state, unconscious state, and dream state. Our invisible self also includes our memories, thoughts, wisdom, and common sense, which is called Buddhi (and pronounced boodhi). When I was growing up and my mother wanted to remind me to pay attention to what I was doing, she would tell me, "Use your Buddhi".

The Atman, or soul -- The Siddhas spent very little time discussing the atman or soul and left this in the realm of the unknowable, which could only be experienced by traversing across the visible and invisible worlds within. They focused, instead, on the visible and the invisible self, performing research and study to discover a system to enable each individual to uniquely pursue that journey within, through the right amount of food to support the physical body, and exercises and meditative practices to support the invisible bodies.

CHAPTER 11

The Architecture of Existence

The foundational elements of Siddha and Ayurveda are conveyed in a native systems architecture that organizes and describes all existence, from the smallest and most subtle elements to the largest. This system also reveals core principles that provide a model for regulating one's life towards optimal health.

The systems architecture of Siddha and Ayurveda are presented in a multi-layered fashion with a particular terminology that describes the elements at each layer. To anyone unfamiliar with Siddha and Ayurveda, this terminology may seem obscure or even "mystical." Our immediate focus, therefore, will be to present and explain this terminology layer by layer.

The first layer is known as *Purusha*. Purusha is best described as consciousness, which expresses itself as will, desire, or motivation.

Purusha is said to give rise to *Prakriti*, the second layer, which represents all material existence that is manifested out of Purusha. A goal or an idea, for example, is representative of Purusha. The expression of that idea in some material form is known as Prakriti. In Indian metaphysics, the entire universe was formed from an idea/thought/will/desire (Purusha) that gave rise to the material existence (Prakriti) that we experiences as matter, energy and information.

Prakriti manifests itself in three forms or aspects of energy. These are known as the Gunas: Sattvic, Rajasic, and Tamasic. The Gunas are the "flavors" of Prakriti, each having its own particular subtle qualities. The Gunas are qualities of subtle energy that cannot be seen, touched, tasted, heard or smelled.

In the next layer of architecture, however, the Gunas manifest in material forms that can be engaged by the five senses. When the Gunas materialize in this way, they are known as the Panchabuthas, or the "five elements." Unlike modern physics, the term "elements" does not refer to elements from the periodic table, but is closer to "states of matter."

The five elements in the Siddha and Ayurveda terminologies, along with their English translations, are below:

Siddha	Ayurveda	English
Akayam	Akasha	Space
Vayu	Vayu	Air
Thee	Agni	Fire
Neer	Jala	Water
Mann	Prithvi	Earth

Practitioners of Siddha and Ayurveda use the interaction of these five elements to understand the dynamics of all nature. In the human body, the Panchabuthas mix with each other in various proportions to form physiological entities such as tissues, as well as to define the whole organism. The Panchabuthas are important in Indian medicine because they give rise to individual constitutions and body types.

The notion of body constitution is presented in the fifth layer through the concept of three *doshas*. Our bodies are space, in which air circulates; they have "fire," expressed as heat; and they have solid structure, made of water and earth. Each of these three components is identified with one of the doshas, which are known as *Vata, Pitta* and *Kapha*:

Three Doshas	Panchabuthas
Vata	Space + Air
Pitta	Fire
Kapha	Water + Earth

Every human body is composed of combinations of these elements, and this combination is central to Siddha and Ayurveda's conception of health and well-being. The specific combination of doshas is present at birth and determines the body type of the individual. This body type is known as the individual's *Prakriti*.

The sixth layer is composed of seven *Dhatus*. The Vata, Pitta, and Kapha constituents of an individual control the nature of that person's Dhatus, which are closely related to tissues in human physiology. The

Dhatus, in the Siddha and Ayurveda terminologies, along with their English translation, are in the chart below:

Siddha	Ayurveda	English
Enbu	Asthi	Bone
Cheneer	Rakta	Blood
Moolai	Majja	Marrow
Sukila/Sronitha	Shukra	Reproductive Tissues
Saram	Rasa	Plasma
Oon	Mamsa	Muscle
Kozhuppu	Meddha	Fat

The seventh layer is the *Kosha,* which is the whole body of the organism. The body includes the *Indriyas,* which are the five senses; *Manas,* which represent the mind; and, the *Karmendriyas,* which represent the physical organs.

CHAPTER 12

Vata, Pitta, Kapha

Siddha and Ayurveda are history's first systems biology, as they provide a multi-layered system to understand all life. The terminology may be foreign, but the organization of Siddha and Ayurveda provides a holistic model describing the whole spectrum of existence, from the metaphysical to the intact living organism.

In the language of Siddha and Ayurveda, the three forces of Vata, Pitta and Kapha, in varying levels, define the state of the Dhatus and the Kosha.

Vata is made up of space and air. Vata control the forces of movement, such as motion of the body, or the flow of receiving and sharing information.

Pitta controls the forces of transformation. This includes digestion, for example, or the conversion of an idea into an action.

Kapha controls the forces that provide storage, structure, or containment. The skeleton of the body, the

81

body's storage of fat, and even memory are controlled by Kapha.

The chart below illustrates the systems biology of Siddha and Ayurveda and their foundational elements:

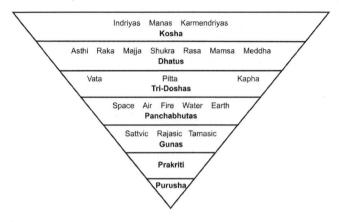

When Siddha medical practitioners look at an individual, they always start with a basic question: "What is this person's basic nature, or Prakriti?" They use a personalized approach to perform diagnostics to get a sense of someone's constitutional makeup, based on his or her combination of *doshas*.

The chart that follows in the next page illustrates the Kosha (the human body), within the large rectangle. The body is defined by the interaction of Vata, Pitta, and Kapha elements. Siddha and Ayurveda recognize that *Karma* (action) leads to *Karma-Phal*, or the "fruits of Karma".

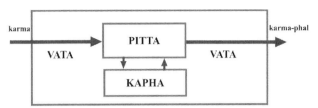

Karma affects Prakriti. For example, the Karma of eating the wrong food or not sleeping enough will lead to Karma-Phal, such as poor skin and being overweight. The Karma-Phal is a symptom of the displacement of the individual's Prakriti. This displaced Prakriti is called *Vikriti*.

Someone's Prakriti may be 30% Vata, 20% Pitta, and 50% Kapha. But due to certain Karmic effects, their Vikriti may become 30% Vata, 50% Pitta, and 20% Kapha. Karma displaced their Prakriti by increasing Pitta and lowering Kapha.

In Siddha and Ayurveda, "health" means an individual's capacity to maintain the body's particular constitution -- Prakriti -- in the midst of stresses and disturbances, through a continuous self-regulating feedback process. This regulatory process is illustrated below:

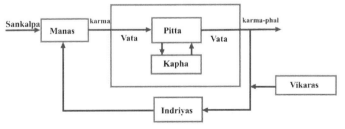

This process begins with a *Sankalpa*, a resolution, to set a goal for optimal health. Optimal health means ensuring that the Kosha (the body) maintains its unique

83

Prakriti, in the midst of *Vikaras* (or disturbances) to the Kosha. Some of these *Vikaras* may be beyond the control of the individual, such as weather changes or moving to a new location. In Siddha and Ayurveda, there is an extensive classification of the different types of Vikaras.

The Manas, the mind, is critical in making the intelligent decisions to input the correct Karma, into the Kosha, which is denoted by the large rectangle in the illustration. The Kosha contains the constitutive elements of Vata, Pitta and Kapha. Based on the Karma, sent into the Kosha, the Vata, Pitta and Kapha elements are adjusted to output Karma-Phal.

The Manas require the *Indriyas* (senses) of smell, taste, hearing, seeing and touch, to be aware of the current Karma-Phal and the Vikaras. Based on the difference between Sankalpa and the Karma-Phal, the Manas make changes to their Karma to adjust the Kosha, to move it away from a state of Vikriti and back to its Prakriti.

The Manas can send certain Karma into the Kosha by varying the intake of certain food, going for a jog, or meditating. This affects the Vata, Pitta, Kapha elements of the Kosha, which results in different Karma-Phal. The process is a constant feedback process, where the Indriyas continually monitor the Karma-Phal and the Vikaras to make adjustments to their Karma, to achieve their Sankalpa.

In summary, there are nine important elements which reflect the core principles of Siddha and

84

Ayurveda. These nine elements are shown in the chart below:

Element
Karmas
Karma-Phal
Vata
Pitta
Kapha
Sankalpa
Manas
Indriyas
Vikaras

PART 4

Systems Theory

CHAPTER 13

The Systems Toolbox

Perhaps the most important knowledge I got from MIT was modern control systems engineering and systems theory. I'm now going to now share this incredible knowledge with you in two important ways. First, you won't need to go to MIT to get it. Second, I've developed some important new aspects so as to unify and clarify principles to make it far more accessible and understandable for everyone.

Systems theory is a toolbox of practical concepts, similar to the scientific understanding of gravity or electromagnetism. It's a very organized and logical way of comprehending the forces that operate in the world. Using systems theory, things that previously seemed random or mysterious can be understood completely and intelligently.

A system is a set of objects or energies working together for a specific goal or purpose. The first step toward understanding systems theory is recognizing the connections between elements that might once have seemed separate but are actually linked together in a system.

Systems can be simple or infinitely complex. A wristwatch, a cow, a human heart, a city, and a washing machine are all systems – as is the Earth itself and even the whole universe. Your body is a system with many subsystems within it. Once you understand how systems work, you can understand how anything works.

To achieve any goal, you will need to understand how *intelligent systems* function. But before we go there, we will begin by understanding how *open systems* work. A toaster and an electric heater are examples of open systems. But the presence of a self-correcting thermostat makes your home heating system an intelligent system.

All systems include five basic elements: *Input, Output, Transport, Conversion,* and *Structure.*

Input is the stuff coming into a system. There can be a single input or multiple inputs. An input can be information, matter, or energy. For example, what did you have to eat today? Did you get any exercise, or did you stay in bed all afternoon? What did you see out the window? What music did you listen to? Whom did you speak with on the phone?

Output is the stuff coming out of a system. This can be a single output or multiple outputs and, like input, output can be information, matter, or energy. The output is the direct result of the inputs (the karma) into a system. If you somehow plugged your toaster into a nuclear power plant, there would be too much electrical input. This would cause a negative output: your toaster blows up. But if you try to light a city with flashlight batteries, you'll get a negative output for the opposite reason: too little input. Depending on the situation, not enough can be as bad as too much.

Transport is the principle of *movement* in a system: the process of information, matter, or energy moving from input to output, from karma to *karma-phal*, from cause to effect. It's the presence or absence of dynamic progress of stuff moving from source to destination. In a computer, transport is the aspect of the machine's process of moving information, bits of ones and zeroes, through the system, from the keyboard (input) to the screen display (output). When purchasing a computer, you may want one that does this very quickly, or you may need to focus on something else.

Conversion in systems theory refers to the process of transforming or *converting* an Input into an Output. The force of conversion changes information, matter, or energy from one form to another. The Central Processing Unit (CPU) of a computer, along with the necessary software, embodies conversion. When you input three symbols on the keyboard ("1 + 1", for example) the CPU converts those symbols into an output, which is "2."

Structure refers to the boundaries, connections, and overall internal environment <u>within</u> which the activities of transport and conversion take place. Structure is sometimes referred to as the storage aspect of a system. A car, whether it's a racer or a SUV, needs a body or frame made of metal, rubber, and plastic. Both a fighter jet and a passenger plane need the fuselage, which holds the cockpit, seats, and engines. Health, physical strength, and emotional stability are structural aspects of a human system.

CHAPTER 14

Open Systems

An *open system* provides a particular Output from a particular Input. Once the Input is set, the Output is set. A basic electric room heater is another everyday example of an open system.

Assuming the heater is plugged into the wall, turning the heater ON and setting it to a particular level – the Inputs of LOW, MEDIUM or HIGH -- results in a certain amount of heat, which is the Output. Transport is the process of transporting electric current from the wall socket into the heater, as well as the heat from the heating coils into the room. Conversion, represented by the heating coils, is what transforms the electrical energy into heat or thermal energy. The Structure element is the entire unit that contains all the components of the system.

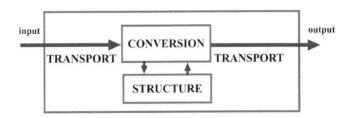

All open systems take in an Input and produce a specific Output. One underlying assumption of open systems is that the Output maintains itself as long as the Input is maintained. Human beings can also be open systems – and there's nothing wrong with that, if it's a conscious choice. The assumption is, for example, you show up to work, work hard and you get as Output a steady income, a stable relationship, and security --- all of which are worthwhile desires. They are certainly what most people hoped for and wanted during much of American history.

But now life is more fluid, unstable and improvisational. Change happens faster. It's no longer easy to even imagine what things were like before laptops and cellphones, even though they've only been around for a relatively short time.

So let's be clear about the relationship between the Input and Output in open systems. An open system provides for a stable and predictable result that is as close to being guaranteed as it can possibly be. If external disturbances occur that affect the result --- the Output --- open systems are not capable of self-correction or self-regulation to adjust the system in order to obtain the original Output.

And once again, there's nothing wrong with getting predictable results from well-understood and conventional actions, provided it's what you really want. But that's becoming more difficult in a world where rapid change is the norm. New technologies and historical changes are demanding that we be more flexible and resilient. For survival and success in that world, an open system existence might no longer be the best choice.

CHAPTER 15

Intelligent Systems

Intelligent systems include four additional elements: a Goal; Disturbances; a Sensor; and, a Controller. These elements enable self-regulation and continuous adjustment of the Input in order to achieve a desired Output that matches the Goal. Using a Sensor and a Controller, this can be achieved in spite of Disturbances to the system.

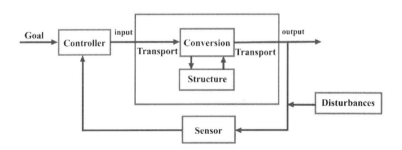

Unlike an open system, an intelligent system begins with a Goal, an intention, (or a *Dharma* or *Sankalpa* as they are referred to in Siddha). Setting this Goal is your responsibility and the Goal must be chosen wisely. The entire process of being "intelligent" exists to achieve that Goal, in spite of any Disturbances that occur.

Disturbances are those things that get in the way of achieving our Goal. They can be physical obstacles, or procrastination, inability to focus, and poor eating habits. In Siddha, obstacles were known as *vikaras*. The ancient Siddhars meticulously itemized all the known vikaras a human may face in a lifetime.

But, here is the secret: if we can use and refine our *Sensors* to know the current Output --- where we are at right now, and then use and develop our *Controller* to measure the difference between where we want to go --- our Goal and our Output to strategically figure out a new Input to affect the forces of Transport, Conversion and Storage to get a desired Output, we can move closer to our Goal. And, this process occurs over time as we go around the loop, and each time getting closer to our Goal.

We do this by "closing the loop" of the open system, by feeding back the Output of the open system to a Sensor, which is used to measure the actual Output. In the Siddha tradition, the Sensor was known as the *Indriyas* of the human body --- the Indriyas were our literal senses of smell, touch, sight, taste and hearing. How well the Sensor can measure is critical to knowing exactly where we are. A poor Sensor can give us an erroneous measure of the Output, and this will affect the decisions of the Controller. In Siddha, the purpose of awareness practices such as meditation, yoga and other spiritual activities was to enhance one's indriyas (sensors). The more our sensors are refined, the closer one can get to the Goal or Sankalpa.

The Controller (or *Manas* in Siddha) literally measures the difference between our Goal and the actual Output to make a decision on what new Input (or Karma) we need to send back into the system to affect changes in the forces of Transport (Vata), Conversion (Pitta) and Storage (Kapha), to get a new Output (Karma-Phal).

The Controller element is perhaps the most important aspect of intelligent systems. The Controller is all about making decisions. By integrating the Goal with information coming in from the Sensors, the Controller makes decisions which result in actions that are new Inputs into the system. These Inputs result in the Transport and Conversion of information, matter, and energy within a Structure, which leads to a new Output. As the sequence takes place and we become aware of the Output from our actions, the Controller draws on this awareness to make a subsequent decision. This results in a new Input. Based on that new Input, the process of Transport and Conversion of information, matter, and energy within a Structure is reiterated and refined.

When Disturbances are encountered, the system must course-correct back toward the Goal. Because this is a continuous process, it's critical that awareness and information – and the decisions that result – can be made on the fly. The more refined our awareness becomes by developing our Sensors, the better our decisions will be. For this reason, spiritual practices, which promote stillness and refinement of our awareness --- the Sensors, enable a clearer perception of what is really taking place and to see the Output with accuracy as it really is. This in turn allows the Controller to make better decisions. When in doubt, therefore, it's important to be still and refine your awareness.

Rather than a strictly spiritual approach, this is a principle of modern systems theory. It is also the essence of Siddha, which teaches stillness as a path to awareness, right decisions, and right action — which together result in the Output of achieving the Goal we desire. In both systems theory and Siddha, this process is what intelligence really means.

At any point in life, we can simply be reactive to what's happening around us, or we can set and approach our goals based on awareness, intention, and intelligence.

Every journey begins with a Goal and some level of awareness. As our awareness becomes more refined, our Controller can make decisions that translate the forces of information, matter, and energy into transport and conversion within a structure that leads toward the goal. The key lies in continuing the process of refining awareness and information, which may even lead to refining or redefining the Goal itself.

CHAPTER 16

An Intelligent System in Action

To make the concept of intelligent systems more real and practical, let's consider a home's central heating system that includes a thermostat. It's a good example of how an intelligent system works. Unlike the open system heater we discussed earlier, this "intelligent" system provides for constant refinement and adjustment of the Input to achieve an Output that matches a specific Goal.

Let's first identify the nine components of the intelligent system using the home heating system as a reference.

Goal: If the desired temperature for the apartment is 78 degrees, that's the Goal. It is achieved when the apartment's actual temperature (the Output) and the selected Goal are equal.

Disturbances: The opposite of a Goal, or the opposition to it, are Disturbances. In the thermostat example, the disturbances could be *a cold draft* from an open window in another room. Resolving Disturbances is the key to achieving the Goal. And, this requires accurate and refined Sensors as well as an effective Controller.

Sensor: The sensor is something that can measure the actual temperature in the room— *a thermometer* – within the thermostat. The Sensor communicates the actual room temperature (the Output) to the Controller. One thing to be aware of is that the sensitivity of the Sensor --- how refined it is in measuring the actual room temperature -- will be critical in achieving the goal of 75 degrees.

Controller: The Controller is the component of the thermostat that receives two pieces of information: 1) what the Goal is --- in this case 75 degrees, and 2) the actual room temperature from thermometer, which is the sensor. The Controller takes these two pieces of information and determines the difference between the Goal temperature and the current temperature.

Transport: The forces of Transport in this case are the flow of heating oil into the furnace. If our current temperature --- the Output --- is too low, say only 60 degrees, then the Input will be to increase the transport (or flow) of heating oil into the furnace. More heating oil, more heat. If this happens and the heat goes too high -- say to 80 degrees -- the Controller will send an Input to shut off the flow of heating oil into the furnace.

Conversion: The furnace takes in the heating oil (matter) and converts it into heat (thermal energy). The more oil, the more heat is produced. Less oil, less heat is produced. No oil, then no heat is produced. It's that simple.

Structure: The Structure is composed of the walls, the floors, the insulation, the beams, and the ceiling. These elements form the structure of the house, which provides a container where the forces of Transport and Conversion come together. Clearly, if you have very well insulated home, then the place will need much less oil to heat, and we can achieve and, more importantly, *maintain* the Goal --- with far less fluctuations. If the home has lots of drafts and poor insulation, heat will escape and the Controller will constantly have to turn on and turn off the flow of oil into the furnace.

Output: The Output is the actual temperature of the room at any point.

The key feature of intelligent systems is that they are always in flux. They are constantly making adjustments. They are sensing, controlling and modulating the input into the open system. "Perfection" is not the objective, but is only an imaginary concept, which is always being approached but is never permanently sustained.

CHAPTER 17

Systems Theory in the Kitchen

Perhaps the best way to understand systems theory is to see it in action in your everyday life. Suppose, for example, you wanted to make a few bowls of soup to serve to some friends on a chilly afternoon.

There are two ways of looking at this example. First, we can imagine making soup as an open system process.

It's very simple. Open a can of soup, put the soup in a pan, and turn on the stove for five minutes.

There are three Inputs: (1) opening the can of soup, (2) putting the soup in the bowl, and (3) turning on the stove for five minutes. The heat activates energies of Conversion to cook the soup. The pan provides the Structure. The Transport is the flow of heat energy through the pan and into the soup. After five minutes the Output is heated soup, which is ready to be consumed.

But suppose you were a more ambitious chef who wanted to make a large amount of soup using an intelligent system. What are the elements relative to the intelligent system of making soup?

Let's start with the Goal. We don't want just any bowl of soup. We want *a tasty, warm bowl of soup* --- this is our Goal. So far, so good.

But with any Goal, Disturbances will arise. There might be a power outage or an overflow of water. The kitchen might run out of a key ingredient. An important employee might suddenly quit in a huff. If something can go wrong, it often will. These are the potential Disturbances.

Remember, we achieve our Goal by overcoming Disturbances through the use of our Sensors and a Controller.

In this case, our five senses are the Sensors. We can observe how the soup is coming along by watching it. We can use our ears to hear if it boiling too much? Does something smell like its burning? We can taste it so see if it has enough salt, or if it's too spicy or needs more sour taste. We can stir it and feel it with our hands to see if it's too thick or coarse. Our senses are fed back to our Controller.

The Controller is you, which includes your experience, your intelligence, and your skill as a chef. Are you getting closer to that tasty, warm bowl of soup? Based on this, you decide what action and inputs you are going to take and keep adjusting the inputs, until you achieve our Goal.

The Inputs could include adding or removal of ingredients, choosing to cover the pan, adding more salt, and increasing the flame.

Transport is the movement of heat and mechanical forces inside the pan, including the simple motion of moving heat as we stir the ingredients.

Next comes the energy of Conversion. The fire that heats the soup embodies this energy.

Structure is provided by the cauldron in which the ingredients are cooked and stirred.

The Goal is reached when, after continuously sensing the soup (tasting it, smelling it, touching it) and making adjustments with our Goal in mind, we get an Output, the tasty bowls of homemade soup.

PART 5

The Rosetta Stone and Beyond

CHAPTER 18

The Bridge Between Two Worlds

Following my doctoral work, I returned to India on a Fulbright grant. While in India, I made a discovery that transformed my life and how I look at the world. New foundations and breakthroughs in human knowledge emerge when disparate systems of knowledge and worlds are connected and unified, and that is exactly the kind of breakthrough I experienced. Technically speaking, I can describe it as identifying the systems theoretic basis of eastern medicine. But I prefer to think of it in more poetic terms, as the discovery of the scientific equivalent of the Rosetta Stone.

Years ago, when visiting the British Museum, I saw the Rosetta Stone on display behind a protective glass casing. It was an amazing experience to see this part of history: a big block of partially broken black and grey stone. The inscriptions on it were still visible. As I studied it, my memory pulled me back to my tenth grade European History class and the teacher who taught us how Napoleon's army in 1799 had unearthed the stone at their Fort Rosetta, during the invasion of Egypt.

Why was this stone important? Why was it protected and displayed with such reverence in the British Museum?

The discovery of the Rosetta Stone provided a gateway between two worlds: ancient and modern, east and west. Up until the time it was decoded, many scholars had difficulty in understanding hieroglyphics, the text used by the Egyptian civilization. While some hieroglyphics had been translated, the vast majority were still a mystery.

On the Rosetta Stone, carved around 190 BC, was a speech or decree by the council of priests, praising Ptolemy V, the new Greek King, recently been put into power as the king of Egypt. This decree was written in three languages side by side: hieroglyphics, an Egyptian script known as Demotic, and classical Greek. The writing on the Rosetta Stone made it possible for scholars to read the decree in three languages simultaneously. In this way, they were able to build a translation and open the door to an understanding of ancient Egyptian history. The stone served as a kind of thesaurus, or translator that provided a *lingua franca* or common language, which opened up the study of Egyptology by deciphering linguistic patterns across the worlds of ancient Egypt to Modern Greek.

In art and science, discoveries such as the Rosetta Stone are compelling not just because they bridge knowledge across the ages but because they interconnect disparate systems of knowledge to reveal a new understanding of existence. Interconnecting and integrating disparate systems reveals new truths that are bigger and different than the truths revealed by any one system alone. We all do this in our own way. And perhaps, the beauty of life lies in our common struggles to find such patterns of connection across the worlds we encounter.

Historically, there has always been a great divide, or even a direct conflict, between the Western scientific establishment and the traditions of Eastern medicine. Simply put, Western authorities felt they "knew it all," not only in the facts they had assembled, but also in the methods they had used to discover and categorize those facts. These methods, as we have discussed, were reductionist. They were hugely effective, as we have also discussed, but they were also limited -- more limited than Western science ever suspected.

While in India on my Fulbright grant, I realized that the principles of systems theory I learned at MIT was fundamentally analogous to the holistic principles of Siddha healing that I had seen my grandmother use. Western science, and especially medicine, was finally catching up with the anti-reductionist, fully integrated view of health and healing that had been the basis of Siddha for 5000 years.

This was truly the intellectual equivalent of the Rosetta Stone. It was the realization that Eastern and Western traditions could now be on the same plane, just as multiple languages, engraved on the Rosetta Stone, were saying the same thing. As I thought about this, I began to understand that even the metaphor of the

Rosetta Stone was inadequate to describe this emerging unity between East and West. This wasn't just the Rosetta Stone. It was the start of the Science of Everything.

CHAPTER 19

The Connective Tissue

Whether consciously or not, every man-made system, simple or complex, has been designed and developed based on the control systems engineering principles we discussed in Part Four. This is a basic principle of all reality. Since the human body is a complex system -- or even a system of systems -- systems biologists are adopting this principle in an effort to design and model complex inter- and intra-system interactions in the human system as a whole.

This approach is transforming biology from a purely experimental field into an engineering discipline. Without conscious awareness on the part of the innovators themselves, the principles of control systems engineering have already produced innovations that enhance the day-to-day lives of almost every human being. The thermostat in home heating systems, cruise control in automobiles, and the autopilot in aircrafts are examples of these innovations. Through a process of iterative understanding and modelling, systems of this kind are created and refined. The human system itself is a product of the principles of control systems engineering in which Nature, as the engineer, has refined and evolved the human system over billions of years.

Identification of the core principles of Control Systems Engineering, as well as itemization of the terminology used to describe those principles, are central components of The Science of Everything. These core principles of control systems engineering are derived from the notion of a system formalized in General Systems Theory, and from concepts of intelligent systems and closed systems based on feedback theory and linear system analysis that integrate concepts of network theory and communication theory.

General Systems Theory (GST) arose from disciplines including biology, mathematics, philosophy, and the social sciences. The Austrian biologist Karl Ludwig von Bertalanffy (1901 – 1972) began to formulate GST in the 1930s. However, his ideas did not receive widespread attention until much later. The aim of GST was to be a "unifying theoretical construct for all of the sciences." Another definition spoke of "a set of related definitions, assumptions, and propositions which deal with reality as an integrated hierarchy of organizations of matter and energy." In other words, a Science of Everything.

Western histories trace the origin of control systems engineering concepts to Greece in approximately 300 BC. These histories refer to the development of the water clock of Ktesibios, which used a float regulator that employed control systems engineering principles. But such histories seem unaware of the development of Siddha and Ayurveda, which were founded on the principles of control systems engineering.

This becomes evident when we juxtapose the terminology of modern control systems engineering with the terminology of Siddha and Ayurveda.

The Table below can be understood as a "Rosetta Stone," demonstrating that the foundations of the systems biology in Siddha and Ayurveda are the same as the principles of control systems engineering.

Control Systems Engineering	Siddha and Ayurveda
Input	Karma
Output	Karma-Phal
Transport	Vata
Conversion	Pitta
Storage	Kapha
Goal	Sankalpa
Controller	Manas
Sensor	Indriyas
Disturbances	Vikaras

This Table is the "Rosetta Stone" that connects Siddha with systems theory.

The terms Karma and Karma-Phal are the same as Input and Output of an open loop system. Vata, Pitta and Kapha are the same as the principles of Transport,

112

Conversion and Storage, which are central to modern systems theory and to Control Systems Engineering. Sankalpa is the Goal that one seeks to achieve. The Manas is the Controller that receives feedback from the Indriyas, which are the Sensor, to assess the current state of the system. Finally, the Vikaras are the Disturbances that are always present, which test the efficacy of a closed loop system to regulate its Input (or Karma) to achieve its particular Goal (or Sankalpa).

CHAPTER 20

Holism and Personalization

The systems biology of Siddha and Ayurveda provides two important features that today's modern Western systems biology seeks to replicate: first, *holism*, and secondly *personalization* within a framework of control systems engineering.

Siddha and Ayurveda developed a holistic understanding of existence from the immaterial to the whole human form. This holism provided a unified model of the whole, progressing from non-existence (Purusha) to material existence (Prakriti), leading to the materialization of subtle energies (Gunas), which then transformed to more grosser forms of matter (the Panchabuthas), that gave rise to a constitutive model called the Tri-Doshas. The three doshas, Vata, Pitta and Kapha, were central to defining the constitution of the body (Kosha), an individual's Prakriti, which affected the tissues (Dhatus) as well as the Kosha's organs, senses and mind.

The systems biology of Siddha and Ayurveda recognized fundamentally that health and well-being had to be personalized, and that there was no "magic bullet" solution, no one-size fits all. The concept of the individual Prakriti provides a mechanism to *personalize* care to find the right therapies that enable the individual to find an optimal state of health that may be very different for another individual. Moreover, there was a clear recognition that health was an ongoing and iterative process, where the individual needed to continually make refinements to their actions, based on sensory feedback from their environment and an intelligent assessment of the results of their actions.

As the Rosetta Stone reveals, the originators of Siddha and Ayurveda created an integrative framework that interconnected its nine concepts: Karma, Karma-Phal, Vata, Pitta, Kapha, Sankalpa, Manas, Indriyas, and Vikaras into a cohesive systems-based regulatory process, that enabled an individual or practitioner to use fundamental principles to manage health. Today, the western world refers to this same process as control systems engineering, conveyed simply in a different language: Input, Output, Transport, Conversion, Storage, Goal, Controller, Sensor and Disturbances.

To the best of my knowledge, this *Science of Everything,* which I first published as "The Control Systems Engineering Foundation of Traditional Indian Medicine: the Rosetta Stone for Siddha and Ayurveda" in the *International Journal of Systems of Systems Engineering,* is the first exposition demonstrating the connection between the core principles of Siddha and Ayurveda and their direct relationship to the concepts of Control Systems Engineering.

At a time when society is recognizing the need for alternatives to the current healthcare system, this Science of Everything provides a much-needed gateway across East and West, integrating ancient tradition and modern science. It provides a common language for understanding.

The ancient rishis and sages of India were not just men dressed in saffron robes but, at a fundamental level, were systems scientists. The irony is that many of the modern "gurus" have forgotten this origin, and today have created their own priesthood completely ignorant of the systems theoretic basis of Siddha and Ayurveda. They monetize this ignorance on multiple levels through their own reductionism giving tid bits of "holy" knowledge to their followers, who they enslave to some singular form of mediation, diet, yoga or ritual practices.

The Science of Everything, therefore, provides the gateway to not only for Western medicine to overcome its own reductionism and embrace Siddha from a solid scientific basis but also to liberate many who have been duped by the "gurus" and priesthood of the East.

PART 6

The System of Your Physical Self

CHAPTER 21

Your Body is an Intelligent System

Intelligent systems as we have seen are based on the desire to achieve a Goal. According to the traditional wisdom of Siddha, the body has a natural intelligence and it inherently knows its goal --- which is known as its *Prakriti* or its *Natural Systems State*. The Natural System State is the unique combination of the forces of Transport, Conversion and Structure inherent to you as an individual. In Siddha, health is defined as you achieving the goal of your body's Natural System State. Most of us are not even aware of our body's Natural System State. Disturbances, moreover, get in the way and perturb us away from our Natural System State.

Therefore, in Siddha the pathway to health begins by knowing our Natural System State – the goal, knowing how Disturbances have moved us away from this goal, and then making the adjustments through the inputs of food, exercise and supplements to bring us back to our Natural System State.

To begin: what is your natural systems state? In terms of systems theory, who is it that you really are? The forces of Transport, Conversion, and Structure affect all forms of matter, energy and information throughout nature. The strength of these forces varies from one life form to another. That strength also varies among individuals – including you -- within a given species.

The importance of these variations is being recognized by Western medicine as better diagnostic tools become available and as genome research reveals the individual character of human DNA. But the concept that every person's physiology is a system with an individualized balance of energies has existed for thousands of years. This became clear to me when I received a Fulbright grant that allowed me to return to India for study of the ancient health tradition known as Siddha.

The Siddhars used their own bodies as experimental laboratories to understand the interaction of three essential forces which they called Vata, Pitta, and Kapha.

As we've seen, it's surprising – or maybe it's not surprising – that the Siddha principles of Vata, Pitta, and Kapha are exact parallels of Transport, Conversion, and Structure. Perhaps systems theory is simply a new terminology for ancient traditional wisdom. Whether we see ourselves as combinations of Transport, Conversion, and Structure -- or of Vata, Pitta, and Kapha -- each of us is a shifting and individualized balance of these energies. It's a balance that needs to be continuously acknowledged, understood, and cared for.

As the forces of nature interact within each of us, some of us have more Transport, others are strongest in Conversion, and still others are dominated by Structure. There are even a few very individuals who have an almost equal presence of each. The varying proportion of these forces is one of the most essential ways in which we are different from each other.

Initially, you need to identify your own Natural System State. Once this has been done, the goal of supporting that state becomes possible. So what is your essential nature? Which forces give direction to your being?

Are you dominated by the force of Transport?

Transport expresses itself as sensitivity to variations in flow, mobility, and movement. If Transport is your dominant force and that force is too high, you may feel nervous and agitated. If it's too low, you could feel very lethargic or depressed. Transport is in charge of everything that moves and is kinetic in our bodies, including the flow of energy and information. Because of this, Transport is regarded as the primary force without which Conversion or Structure could not function.

When Transport is not functioning correctly, all the other forces can go awry.

- Are you extremely uncomfortable in cold weather?
- Do you often juggle several activities at once?
- Do you think and talk quickly?
- Do you prefer spontaneity over scheduling?
- Do you tend toward dry skin and hair?

- Are you naturally thin, and do you lose weight easily?
- Do you grasp new ideas quickly, but wish you could remember more of what you learn?
- Do you impulsively start working on projects without thinking them through?
- Do you sometimes skip meals or forget to eat?
- Are you basically optimistic and enthusiastic?

Are you dominated by the force of Conversion?

Conversion manifests as sensitivity to variations in physiological processes such as metabolism and digestion, as well as analytical thinking and decision-making. If the forces of Conversion are not functioning well, you can experience health and emotional problems associated with the inability to convert and transform elements of Matter, Energy and Information.

- Do you very strongly dislike hot weather?
- Are you detail oriented and exceptionally good at processing information and data?
- Do you think things through before taking action?
- Do you metabolize food quickly and efficiently?
- Do view competition as an enjoyable challenge?
- Does your weight fluctuate?
- Do you prefer to have meals on a set schedule?
- Do you become impatient with yourself or others?
- Do you enjoy turning ideas into applications?
- Are your eyes especially sensitive to sunlight?

Are you dominated by the force of Structure?

Structure is the principle of containment for matter, information, and energy. Men and women who are Structure dominant are naturally able to sustain and tolerate more than other people. Structure forces foster relaxation and calm, and an aura of security. But when Structure is out of balance it can manifest as stubbornness or isolation.

- Do you have a broad body frame?
- Do you tend to be overweight?
- Do you prefer not to move around or travel?
- Are you often called upon to help others?
- Are you not bothered by either hot or cold weather?
- Do you have exceptionally good physical stamina?
- Is your preferred learning style slow and steady?
- Do you easily retain what you've learned?
- Do you take your time moving between activities?
- Do you often have sinus infections or colds?
- Do you try to speak precisely and emphatically?

CHAPTER 22

Identifying Disturbances

Disturbances are part of any journey, including the journey of our lives. Once you become aware of your Natural System State, it's your responsibility to keep that state in balance, despite any turbulence you encounter.

But at any given moment you are likely not operating at the peak of your Natural System State. So how are you right now? How are you feeling today? Is everything going well in your life? Do you feel upbeat and cheerful or do you feel down in the dumps? Are you feeling healthy? Or are you catching a cold?

As a unique and dynamic person, you are not going to be feeling the same every day. Here are some questions to help you get a handle on what the forces of Transport, Conversion, and Structure are doing in your system, right now. Your answers will help you determine which forces are "off-course." You can then decide how you want to bring that force back into alignment.

Are your Transport forces undergoing disturbances?

- Have you been feeling anxious or overly excited?
- Is your energy level noticeably uneven?
- Are you feeling depressed, or do you have bursts of energy so intense that you have a hard time calming down?
- Do you have any dry spots, chapped, or cracked skin?
- Is your lower GI tract upset? Are you having bouts of diarrhea or constipation? Do you experience gas or bloating?
- Are you forgetting to eat, or are you losing weight?
- Is cold weather bothering you more than usual?
- Are you having difficulty concentrating or finishing projects?
- Are you having joint or arthritic pain?
- Have you been making any impulsive decisions?
- Do you have trouble falling asleep or staying asleep?

Are your Conversion forces undergoing disturbances?

- Are you putting pressure on yourself or others?
- Are you having upper GI problems?
- Are you suffering from heartburn or a sore throat that your doctor thinks is caused by acid reflux?
- Is an aversion to heat becoming more intense?
- Do you need stronger sunglasses than previously?
- Are you easily angered or often impatient?
- Have you become noticeably critical of others?

- Do you drink large amounts of water or other beverages?
- Do you have more rashes or cold sores than usual?
- Do you have feelings of jealousy or need to get even?

Are your Structure forces undergoing disturbances?
- Are you having sinusitis, allergies, or congestion?
- Are you able to keep your weight under control?
- Do you crave carbs, chocolate, or other sweets?
- Do you want to sleep all the time?
- Do you have a white coat on your tongue?
- Are you generally feeling lethargic and dull?
- Do you often procrastinate?
- Do you accumulate things you don't need?
- Are you finding it difficult make changes in your life?
- Do you respond to stress with hostility?

By learning which forces are disturbed, you can be the Controller, making adjustments to Inputs that will bring you back to your Natural System State. But the first step is to correctly assess what's wrong. What is the true nature of the disturbance? Be real. Don't look for an easy answer, neither in reductionist science nor in reassuring New Age mysticism.

CHAPTER 23

Dealing With Disturbances

When disturbances arise between where you are now and arriving at your goal, you'll need to make some adjustments. That means eliminating any imbalances that have destabilized the forces of Transport, Conversion and Structure, and optimizing those forces instead.

Optimizing the Forces of Transport. Transport is expressed through movement. When it's in balance, Transport presents itself as joy, grace, agility and enthusiasm. Both systems theory and Siddha identify three Inputs as essential for Transport to function at an optimal level: warmth, rhythm and lubrication.

Stay Warm
Our bodies, particularly our muscles, work far more efficiently when they are warmed up before any kind of activity or exercise. Muscles contract and relax faster when they are warm. Warmth gives your muscles greater

agility, speed, and strength. Warming up is like an insurance policy, decreasing the possibility of injury while also allowing you a greater degree of motion. If you are warm, your blood vessels are dilated, and this reduces stress on your heart and increases the flow (movement) of blood throughout your body. Blood is the key transporter of nutrients in your body. When you stay warm, your blood is able to be more efficient and deliver more oxygenated blood, making your entire system more effective to support motion at multiple levels. It also enables oxygen in your blood to be transported at a greater speed.

Your joints are key to movement and motion. Staying warm enables you to have a wide range of motion. Stiffness, for example, is a symptom that Transport is not working right. Warmth increases production of synovial fluids in your joints, serving to reduce friction, to support that range of motion. Greater range of motion gives you the greater confidence to try new things in a safe manner. Staying warm helps your body secrete the hormones that enable energy production, which is key to Transport. Exhaustion is another symptom telling us that the forces of Transport are not functioning right.

Movement can be erratic and chaotic, methodical and elegant, or graceful and intelligent. Staying warm enables nerve impulses to be transported at greater speeds, resulting in greater focus. This focus in turn will support the right level of concentration in a relaxed manner to provide support for graceful motion.

In order to thrive, Transport needs the Input of warmth. Think about your car on the coldest winter morning. Most of us will go out and warm it up before driving off. The warmth we are talking about is inner warmth, inside of the engine, inside of the car, inside of you. Warm friends, a warm home, and a warm disposition all fuel your inner forces of Transport. By doing those things that build such inner warmth, you directly support the optimal functioning of Transport.

Stay in Rhythm

A sense of rhythm is the ability to move your body to a regular beat. Rhythm or regularity is key to optimal motion and Transport. A person who dances well moves to a regular rhythm. A great drummer follows a great beat. Musicians often train with a metronome, an instrument that puts out a constant beat, to help them keep their rhythm. One of my mentors Frank Zane, the great body builder, taught me to lift weights to a metronome, or to a beat. When one does this, it makes it much easier, and more fluid. One can move and Transport with greater ease.

Because the force of Transport drives so many important body processes, it requires this level of regularity. Breathing, digestion and elimination are all dependent on proper rhythm and regularity. Having a regular schedule, eating at regular times, and sleeping and waking regularly is all about being in rhythm, which makes Transport far more effective. As someone said, "repetition is the mother of skill."

Siddha masters recommended that their students follow a schedule--early to bed, early to rise, routinized mealtimes, and play and work at particular hours. They were very demanding about the need for such regularity. In fact, in all spiritual practices, regularity is more important than the length of practice. Some people will meditate for 2 hours for a few weeks, and then stop, without any semblance of discipline. It is better to do less, but with consistency to achieve the best results. The highest level of rhythm and regularity is critical for the force of Transport.

In our breathing, the forces of Transport manifest themselves most clearly. Without breath our entire being ceases to exist. In the Bible, it is said that life began when God breathed into Adam's nostrils. The breath we have has a rhythm and regularity. That rhythm regularizes our pulse, our heart beat and our nerves. Emotions such as anger change our rhythm, and affect the forces of Transport. Every time we move or exercise, this is an exercise in breath. Breath is a gateway for us to see the force of Transport in action, and a way to measure our regularity moment to moment.

Stay Lubricated

Smooth and agile motion is supported by lubrication. All machines move better when they are well lubricated. Think about it. Your car will not move without oil and regular oil changes. Neither will you. To support Transport, your body needs to be well lubricated. Lubrication supports our joints, enables cellular motion, lessens buildup of plaque in our arteries, and ensures that nerve impulses fire right.

Across a range of internal cellular processes, Transport needs lubrication. Without lubrication, the machinery of our bodies begin to squeak, get tight, rust, and motion stops. That squeaking door in your kitchen needs some oil. The stiffness in your joints would also benefit from some lubrication. Lubrication removes friction and ensures long-life of machinery, including your inner machinery.

The right kinds of oils and fats, and proper hydration support that lubrication. Wonderful research is being done and continues to be done on the value of different kinds of wholesome plant and animal based fats and oils. Doing your own research on them can prove to be invaluable. Healthy fats and oils play an overall role in supporting the forces of Transport. They contribute to an increase in energy and help us gain muscle mass. They also support the functioning of our heart, lungs, brain and digestive organs --- all components involved in Transport. The right lubrication makes our internal motors of motion that move air, blood, electrical signals run with ease and minimal friction. Healthy fats help protect our heart, an important motor-like pump, from cardiovascular diseases.

Our bones and skeletal structure keep us moving as we walk and run. Lubrication of the right kinds has been shown to strengthen bone density and reduce incidences of fractures, so as we age, we can still keep moving. Your skin is a major organ of transporting fluids and substances such as hormones, lymph, and water.

Hydration, which is a form of lubrication, is key to supporting movement of those fluids and substance to support the forces of Transport.

The right kind of lubrication supports internal cellular signaling, and the right signaling is key to cellular communication. Wrong communication results in illness and disease. Repeated studies have shown the value of lubrication at the cellular level to protect against various forms of cancer. Lubrication protects our machinery from rusting --- a process known in chemistry as oxidation.

That bicycle chain in your backyard has oxidized and is rusty. Put some oil on it, clean it up, and it's as good as new. Similarly, oils that are known as anti-oxidants can help remove the "rust" from our internal motors so Transport forces are able to glide smoothly. Nerve signaling, a type of cellular signaling, affects mood disorders. Stress affects nerve signaling and may result in increased depression and anxiety. The right kind lubrication increases levels of serotonin in the body. Serotonin makes people feel good and puts them in a relaxed state. Being relaxed supports agile Transport.

Optimizing the Forces of Conversion. The forces of Conversion are expressed as intensity and determination. When three key Inputs are present, Conversion presents itself as enterprising, brave, intelligent, ambitious, confident, and self-disciplined. These three Inputs are essential for Conversion to function at an optimal level: being cool, regulated and clean.

Stay Cool

Intensity doesn't need more intensity. Fighting fire with fire doesn't work here. The process of Conversion does the job of converting Matter, Energy and Information from one form into another. These processes all require "heat." However, in order to operate efficiently, they also need proper cooling.

A nuclear reactor, which is able to convert nuclear fission to thermal energy, is a classic example of Conversion. But a nuclear reactor needs those big cooling towers we see when pictures of reactors are shown. Your hot kitchen needs an exhaust system to keep it cool; your computer needs a fan to keep it cool.

Men and women with rapid metabolism and fiery dispositions – expressions of Conversion in action -- need to stay cool, in both mind and body, to balance their internal engines. Those with Conversion dominance need to look to the external world for ways to input cooling factors. This is different from those with a Transport dominance, who need to Input ways of increasing internal warmth.

Conversion dominant people need to avoid "hot situations" that can cause tempers to flare; they need to learn to "cool down" during those times when the intensity of action (during tough business negotiations for example) becomes too extreme. Staying Cool ensures that you don't overheat and burn up your internal engines, which are the power source of Conversion.

Warm-blooded animals sweat (like a human) or pant (like a dog) to dissipate heat through water evaporation. Sometimes it's easy just to cool off by going under a nice

132

shaded tree or get some water on us. Other times it may be good just to take a vacation, "chill out" and go to cooler areas. Sometimes just sitting and watching the sunrise or sunset and other of Nature's beauty can serve to provide the cool to calm down and support the forces of Conversion, to remove the "heat."

Stay Regulated

The forces of Conversion are involved in the process of transformation and transduction. They convert energy from one form to another. The retina in your eyes convert light, electromagnetic radiation, to chemical impulses which are transduced to "see" the world. The engine in your car converts chemical energy to rotational mechanical energy.

This all involves many systematic and interconnected processes that need to be regulated correctly, with great sensitivity, to make sure that the inputs are converted to the right outputs.

If your retina does not transduce correctly, you get a blurred vision. If your car engine's pistons are not regulated with the right mixture of fuel and air to fire correctly, your car's motion could be accompanied by loud backfiring. All engines need to regulate their activity from action to rest, from focused work to regular maintenance --- in short they need to be in balance across the forces of motion and stillness.

Conversion can create a tendency to push too hard. They gravitate toward being on the go all the time, with extreme activity and little rest. If they don't learn how to regulate their activities, they run the risk of "burning up" and "burning out". Sometimes, this inability to regulate their own internal engines, results in an attempt to control everything, and everybody, in their environment. It would be better for them to learn how to control and regulate their own activities.

It can be difficult for a conversion dominant person to "let go" and relax with themselves and others. Their tongues can become harsh and mean --- an inappropriate way to control a situation, because in reality they are not able to control themselves. Extremes of this out-of-control behavior include throwing tantrums, becoming manipulative, all of which reflect a lack of self-regulation, which can backfire much like a car engine, whose internal pistons, misfire. High performance jet engines are designed to function well. They are able to operate across a wide range of temperatures and altitudes. They can regulate their engine performance across a variety of conditions, can adjust and adapt. Conversion forces require proper regulation to ensure their optimal functioning.

Regulation includes setting bounds of operation. Those who are dominated by Conversion forces can achieve great success if they are given, or create for themselves, internal and external boundaries. A high performance car also has its boundaries, if you "red-line" above a certain number of RPM's, the engine will conk out. The forces of Conversion operate well within their lower and upper bounds.

Work and rest are therefore equally important for these forces of Conversion. Forces of Conversion, like a motor can "be on" all the time, and not know when to stop. Men and women with strong Conversion forces have a tendency to overdo just about everything. They can work too hard, they can exercise too much, and they can over-do it with their attention to detail. Our Conversion dominant friends sometimes need to relax and stop competing. They need to learn to modulate their behavior, keeping everything more reasonable and moderate.

Regulating your behavior also implies being able to "surrender" and "go with flow" at appropriate times. Those with dominant Conversion forces can sometimes appear always to be on "high alert" in terms of a need to control the people and things in their environment. They need to learn how to regulate their behavior by stepping back and surrendering. It's essential to know when to stop, relax, rest, and shut down.

Stay Clean

Like any high performance engine, forces of Conversion thrive in a clean environment. This includes both high quality fuel and a clean internal mechanism. People dominated by Conversion need to be very careful about what they input into their bodies. Whole foods, organic and without preservatives and additives are wonderful because they provide "clean" fuel.

There is an emerging movement among pioneering food manufacturers in formalizing the definition of such clean foods through a newly developed Certified C.L.E.A.N. international standard, which I helped to facilitate using a systems-based approach that defines such foods as ones that have multiple attributes including being safe, non-GMO, organic, and having high bio-availability of nutrients. Keeping an eye out for such clean foods can serve to support Conversion.

Food combining is another wise strategy for ensuring effective transformation within our digestive systems. Slow-cooked foods, in many ways pre-digested, make it easy for our internal engine to absorb nutrients. In addition, regular and moderate fasts allow our engines to clean and heal themselves by supporting the body's own self-healing processes.

Optimizing the Forces of Structure. Structure brings stability, and stability is essential for survival. Men and women in whom Structure is dominant tend to have stability in their own lives and they like to provide it for others as well. The three Inputs that encourage Structure's optimal performance are: being dry, active and flexible.

Stay Dry

The force of Structure provides containment and support. When a home is built, the foundation represents the Structure force that holds the entire house. If the foundation (or basement) is damp or wet, the building's entire infrastructure is at risk.

Excessive dampness in your body's foundation can show up as cysts, tumors, chronic sinus infections, and yeast infections. Dryness can also have the benefit of slightly raising the body's temperature, creating a structural environment that is resistant to viruses and bacteria. A dry sauna, for example, can be ideal for supporting Structure.

Stay Active

Use it or lose it. Any physical structure, including the human body, gets stronger the more it gets used and stimulated. If you don't use your muscles, your skeletal structure, you atrophy. Structures that are not used are vulnerable to decay and rust. Various types of stimuli are critical in keeping a structure activated.

At the cellular level, the cell membrane and cytoskeleton, support the structure of the entire cell. Nature ensures that this structure is under constant stimuli to keep it vigilant and active so it supports the cell structure. Such activity increases the number of macrophages. Macrophages enhance the immune system and support structure by killing invading bacteria and viruses.

Physical activity also increases blood flow, allowing antibodies to move through your system and attack and remove bacteria and viruses. For those who suffer from inflammation, anti-inflammatory cytokines, which are the cell-to-cell signaling molecules, are themselves activated by physical activity. These molecules have a beneficial effect in promoting anti-inflammatory effects. This is one of the important benefits that come from being active because chronic inflammation causes most of the degenerative diseases such as cancer.

The forces of Structure provide framework and inertia. This inertia can also result at its extremes in laziness, moodiness, and immobility. Sometimes those who are dominant in the forces of Structure "just don't feel like moving." Inertia and a lack of movement can contribute to a sense of depression or lethargy. Exercise and physical activity stimulates neurotransmitters in the brain to make one feel happier, less moody, and less depressed. Inertia is also implicated in osteoporosis, a structural disorder that causes bone loss. Exercise and physical activity is prescribed as a treatment for those who have osteoporosis or are in danger of getting it because it can help prevent and arrest the problem.

In order to hold things, Structure itself requires containment. The tendency to "holding on" often spells out issues with weight. Being active is a great controlling and modulating factor to manage one's weight. There is no better cure for the inertia and laziness of Structure forces than to boost one's energy level through physical activity. Diseases such as diabetes manifest when the forces of Structure go to its extremes of containment. Being active can be help deal with this condition. Activity helps makes the body more sensitive to insulin, to support burning of glucose e.g. calories. This helps to lower blood glucose and stop sugar spikes. Diabetics who exercise have been shown to need less insulin or medication than those who don't.

People with Structure dominance can also become too complacent and reliant on the status quo. They have a tendency to not want to "let go" of anything, including relationships and objects. They can "hold onto" relationships, situations, and things that no longer have value in their lives. Activity—getting out in the world, meeting new people, and trying new things—is a way of fighting this tendency.

Stay Flexible

Structure contains the elements of water and earth. Structures composed of water and earth can get stuck, muddy, swampy, and immobile. The most powerful structures in the world are not rigid, but flexible. If something is too hard, it can become brittle, and just shatter and break. In civil engineering, when larger structures are built, particularly in earthquake zones, they are designed to sway and to be flexible; sometimes they are even put on rollers, so they will move with the wave of the earthquake. The largest modern skyscrapers in the world now actually flex like pine grass in the wind.

This is a wonderful example of how flexibility can provide additional strength and make structures strong enough to withstand even the most powerful of Nature's forces. Similarly, flexibility is key for someone who is Structure dominant. If you become too stiff, you too can break or fall apart by life's continual and ongoing disturbances and changes. If you become too set in your ways, you might end up feeling as though you are stuck in a quagmire that resembles nothing so much as a muddy swamp.

Flexibility gives structures greater strength. Joints and fascia are particularly improved by flexibility. Blood flow can be increased by flexibility exercises such as stretching, which removes toxins and waste products that can cause a structure to "squeak" and get stiff.

Stretching the joints also results in improved blood flow, which, in turn, can cause slight increases in tissue temperature; this supports circulation and increases the flow of rich nutrients to the joints creating greater elasticity and higher levels of structural performance.

Flexibility allows structures to be more effective in dealing with environmental disturbances. My grandmother used to tell a story of two kinds of trees. One tree would bend when a river flooded and was able to go back to its original shape once the waters receded. The other tree would resist the flood and would ultimately be broken, ripped out from its roots. Structures that bend are more likely to survive.

Scientists have repeatedly shown how flexible structures can adjust themselves to reduce drag. It is clear that that unlike rigid structures for which an increase in velocity causes a squared increase of drag, the increase in drag for a flexible object is significantly lower.

Above all, it's your responsibility – and your opportunity – to become fully aware of the dominant energies of your being, and your Goal is to keep them in balance to support your Natural System State, not someone else's. Remember too that balance is not a passive state. It's achieved through strong action, and strong action is required to sustain it as well. There's a teaching by Vivekananda, one of India's contemporary spiritual masters, that alludes to this. Despite his metaphysical orientation, Vivekananda advised his students that if there was a choice between doing 50 pushups or meditating for 50 minutes, do the pushups!

PART 7

The Science of Everything at the Movies

Everyone's life is unique, yet all our lives have shared experiences. It occurred to me that watching movies is a shared experience for millions of people. And the content of many films, including some of the most successful ones, seem to very clearly use elements of systems theory. So discussing films as a way to illuminate systems theory seems like a good way to draw on an experience that millions of people have shared – that is, watching a movie.

The three films in this Part have been big successes critically and commercially. If you've seen them, I hope these discussions are revealing about the films as well as analogous events from real life. If you haven't seen them, perhaps now you'll be inspired to do as soon as possible for your own benefit. As the hero of *Gladiator* says, "What you do today will echo in eternity!"

CHAPTER 24

Gladiator

"A general of the Roman army is betrayed and becomes a slave and then a gladiator. And eventually he confronts the evil emperor who betrayed him in man-to-man combat."

This is how one of the characters in *Gladiator* summarizes the plot of the film. It's a good start but there's a lot more to say from a systems perspective.

Gladiator is the story of the Roman military commander Maximus, played by Russell Crowe. The film introduces Maximus as a citizen soldier who has left his farm, his wife, and their child in order to lead the Roman army. His deeply personal goal is simply to win the war against the barbarian hordes and return to his family.

But Maximus is also given a more public and political one by the dying emperor Marcus Aurelius. The emperor wants to designate Maximus as his heir in place of

Commodus, the emperor's corrupt son played by Joaquin Phoenix.

Commodus recognizes Maximus as a threat when Marcus Aurelius informs him of his intention to designate Maximus as his heir, thereby denying Commodus the possibility of becoming emperor.

Gladiator is an excellent resource for understanding the elements of systems theory and seeing how they play out in a complex narrative. Let's look at these elements one by one.

Goal: Commodus must be destroyed. This is Maximus' primary goal but – unlike Commodus' murder of Marcus Aurelius – Maximus does not simply kill his adversary even when he has the chance. Maximus knows that he must win the support and loyalty of the Roman people before real political change can take place. The balance of the film shows how Maximus gains that understanding and puts it into action.

Disturbances: In systems theory disturbances are the opposite of goals – the opposing energy. Commodus is Maximus' major disturbance. Systems theory includes two closely related elements that are basic to overcoming disturbances and responding effectively to them. These elements are the *sensor* and the *controller*. Just as disturbances are expressions of change, sensors and controllers are also dynamic in nature. They need to be upgraded from time to time as conditions change, and as you change during progress toward your goal.

Sensors: The sensors are those things that provide Maximus insight into what is going on so he can make decisions to guide him towards his goal. Early in the film, Maximus' sensors are not completely adequate to the hostile environment and the disturbances it presents. However, they provide unreliable intelligence. Later Maximus will come to rely and refine his own intuition and senses, even in the midst of being mortally wounded, to meet his goal.

Controller: Based on the information derived from sensors, a controller derives and implements a powerful action-oriented strategy. Initially when the gruff former gladiator Antonius Proximo purchases Maximus, as a slave, Maximus undergoes brutal training in Proximo's gladiatorial school. But Proximo soon becomes a mentor to Maximus. Specifically, Proximo once and for all diverts Maximus from a simple desire to kill Commodus for revenge. He makes it clear to Maximus that there is a larger issue that has to be addressed. Maximus has to be successful in the gladiatorial arena, and he needs to be entertaining while he does that. He has to win over the Roman crowd, because once they are on his side he can turn them against Commodus. This is the kind of insight a controller can provide.

Input: Inputs are the actions dictated by the decisions of the controller. In this case, they are the literal actions that Maximus takes to achieve his goal. Initially, Maximus knows that his actions must be congruent with everything that Proximo has taught him.

144

He has learned to fight well as a gladiator and win in the arena – and he must also gain the allegiance of the people by exciting and entertaining them. His actions are no longer about killing Commodus. It's about winning fights in the coliseum as a way to gain the final victory. Once Input is clear, the dynamic aspects of systems can manifest themselves. The foundations are in place, and meaningful action toward the goal expresses itself through the principles of *Transport, Conversion*, and *Structure*.

Transport: Transport is movement. In the early part of the film Maximus took some hard hits after being betrayed and sold into slavery. He becomes inert, depressed and lethargic. As Maximus interacts with Proximo and his comrades in the gladiator's school, he begins to move himself and eventually those around him as well. He reactivates the power of leadership that he showed in the film's early scenes as the general of the Roman army. He becomes an organizer and an inspiration to his fellow gladiators. He turns his fellow gladiators into a small, highly disciplined army – and he is once again ready to be a general and moves them into action towards his goal.

Conversion: Gladiator's fight scenes are the expression of the principle of conversion. Through each victory in the colosseum, Maximus converts the masses in the audience to become his loyal fans. Commodus challenges him to single combat in the arena. But the combat will be anything but fair. Commodus

145

treacherously wounds Maximus in the side just before the fight. Still, Maximus kills Commodus in the arena in a carefully choreographed action sequence. With his dying words, Maximus asks for the republic to be reinstated. The audience is converted to become loyal followers of his leadership, thereby enabling him to achieve his goal.

Structure: The coliseum and the crowd that populates it form the structural element of *Gladiator's* system. They are essential to the action, but they don't directly participate in it. The coliseum and the audience provide the structure within which the Transport (the movement) and Conversion (the fight) occur.

Output: Within the storyline of the film, *Gladiator's* Output is Maximus' winning over the audience to his side. The success of this Output helps Maximus assess whether he's heading towards his sacred goal – the restoration of the Roman republic. But it's interesting to note that the Output of the film exists in another form as well.

Whatever the goals of the characters in Gladiator may be, the movie itself is also a system with goals of its own. The film's goals include, first and foremost, the need to make a profit, and also to be artistically satisfying to the audience. Few movies are able to achieve both these objectives and Gladiator is one of the few.

CHAPTER 25

Apollo 13

Apollo 13 is a film based on a lunar space flight that was aborted when an emergency occurred on the spacecraft. The film was a commercial success and an even greater critical success. It received nine academy award nominations in 1995, winning in two technical categories. It won many other prizes as well.

Goal: Initially, the Goal of the Apollo 13 spaceflight is a landing on the moon. The astronauts will collect samples of moon rocks and bring them back to Earth. In the film's opening sequence astronaut Jim Lovell, played by Tom Hanks, hosts a party at his home to watch the first moon landing by Neil Armstrong. Lovell is scheduled for a moon flight – Apollo 14 -- but not until another crew goes to the moon first. We sense that his personal Goal is going to the moon, and his disappointment that he was not the first person to get there and that he will not be going to the moon for at least a year or more.

In the next scene, however, Lovell learns that he and his two companion astronauts – Ken Mattingly (Gary Sinise) and Fred Haise (Bill Paxton) – have been moved up to become the crew of Apollo 13. At this point the Goal of the film as a whole and Jim Lovell's personal Goal become one and the same. It's all about making Apollo 13 a successful flight to the moon.

Disturbances: It's just one thing after another. From the first moment until the last, *Apollo 13* shows unexpected problems appearing. Most of them are of a technical nature, involving the operation of the rocket, the ability to complete the mission, or even to survive Disturbances like a breakdown in the oxygen supply or the extreme heat of reentry to the Earth's atmosphere. There are also interpersonal disturbances among the characters, both those in the rocket and on the ground in the mission control site.

Sensors: Just as there are lots of Disturbances in *Apollo 13*, there are plenty of sensors. In fact, there is a large room full of hard-working nerds in the mission control facility who are dedicated to keeping track of everything that happens on the flight and to identifying anything that goes wrong. Since plenty of things do go wrong, the sensors have an important role in the film. Some of them are grouchy, some of them are charmingly insightful, but they're all totally dedicated and extremely competent. They make us proud of them.

148

Even the dials and gauges in the rocket's cockpit – sensors in a literal way – play dramatic roles when, for example, they indicate the temperature inside the module or rising levels of life-threatening carbon dioxide. The Sensor gauges are our friends and advocates, just like the nerds back in Houston.

Controller: Apollo 13 is definitely a Controller's movie. Jim Lovell, of course, is a Controller in his role as commanding officer of the mission. But the most prominent Controller in the film is Flight Director Gene Kranz, played by Ed Harris, who supervises the technicians in the Mission Control Center. Kranz is probably one of the clearest personifications of a Sensor in any movie ever made.

Input: The character of Gene Kranz creates a strategy for the mission that has become the film's signature line of dialogue: "Failure is not an option!" At one point he challenges the technicians to fit a square piece of equipment into a round container: in other words, to put a square peg into a round hole. And they do it too. We don't see exactly how they do it, but we know that the software that Kranz downloads into the move is going to work, because failure is not an option. He does something like this many times during *Apollo 13*. We never find out how he does it, or what his experience and credentials are, but Ed Harris makes it perfectly believable.

149

Transport: This is the kinetic element of the film. It's all the scenes in which action is happening and movement taking place. Certainly there are images that obviously provide this component. The sequence of the rocket's fiery takeoff, the sequence in which the module flies low above the moon's surface, and the reentry of the vehicle through the Earth's atmosphere are a few examples. The whole movie is a mixture of the claustrophobic environment of the rocket and the Mission Control Center, and the infinite vastness of outer space.

Conversion: When the lunar module starts its descent to Earth, the three-man crew has learned to work perfectly together through the many Disturbances that have arisen.

Structure: The physical settings of Apollo 13 are unusually important, perhaps because there are so few of them. They mean a lot to us as viewers because they play a direct role in the action. We come to feel at home in the mission control center and the lunar module, especially when the characters go for days without shaving or sleeping.

Output: The Goal was not attained – but as sometimes (or often) happens the original goal was adjusted or even replaced. We see these adjustments happening all through Apollo 13, and the ability of the characters to respond to them is another thing we're urged to admire. The whole meaning of *Apollo 13* can be summed up in phrases like "things always happen for a reason" or "things turn out for the best." That such a successful film could be built on those kinds of sayings is testimony to the power of systems theory, at least when it's applied by very talented people.

CHAPTER 26

Joy

Joy is a very different kind of film from *Gladiator* and *Apollo 13*. In the language of Hollywood, Joy is what's called a "women's picture." The lead role and the principal supporting roles are played by women, and the primary audience for the film is also female.

Gladiator shows us the hero, Maximus, learning to fight in the arena. We see Russell Crowe, a major star, being instructed and upbraided by his mentor, Proximo. These scenes fulfill one of the anthropologist Joseph Campbell's major criteria for the development of an epic hero. That is, the hero must descend to the depths. He must seem to lose his heroic stature. In this way, he can rise again to greater heights than ever before.

An updated, female version of this happens in Joy. Instead of Russell Crowe being treated like a slave, we see Jennifer Lawrence – currently the premier actress of her generation – cleaning up spilled juice and demonstrating a mop in the parking lot of a KMart store.

Jennifer Lawrence hits bottom, and then rises to the financial heights. But instead of restoring the Roman republic or flying to the moon in a rocket, she gets rich by inventing a new kind of mop.

Goal: Joy Mangano (Jennifer Lawrence) was a precocious, extremely imaginative child who did very well in school. She loved to give form to her ideas by building models and acting out fantasies. But now, after marrying a failed lounge singer and having two children, she's trapped in a tedious job. She also lives in a house with her extended family of quirky relatives who are alternately funny and obnoxious, and who are closer to poor than rich.

Joy's personal, internal goal is to recapture the excitement and imagination of her childhood. In fact, we see a dream sequence in which Joy's own childhood self appears and makes that goal clear to her.

Joy's external goal is to get herself and her family out of their financial problems. After showing us Joy's predicament in the first twenty minutes of the film, we watch Joy have an epiphany when a glass of wine is spilled on the teak wood deck of a wealthy woman's yacht. At that moment, with her instincts as a creative engineer, Joy has an idea for a revolutionary mop design. The rest of the film depicts the twisting path toward the realization of her goals.

Disturbances: Joy is a creative and entrepreneurial woman but she's held back by her domestic situation. Her crazy family members aren't exactly happy with living hand to mouth in a crowded house, but it's what they're used to. They've developed so-called coping mechanisms. Joy's mother spends all day in bed watching soap operas. Her husband stays in the basement practicing his singing. Her sister has developed a personality based on humiliating Joy. Her father runs an auto parts company that barely stays afloat.

At the start of the film, these are Joy's Disturbances. More specifically, they're her distractions. They keep her disconnected from her true talents. As she begins to break free, new Disturbances crop up that are more than just distracting. But within *Joy* as a system, living uncomfortably in a crowded house is seen as really, really awful. It may even be worse than death, because there's nothing grand about it. It's low comedy rather than high tragedy.

Sensors: One of Joy's biggest problems early in the film is the complete absence of reliable Sensors. Surrounded by dysfunctional people who deeply misunderstand the real world, Joy's own perceptions are numbed by trying to keep the whole thing afloat.

Joy may not live completely in a dream world like her mother watching soap operas, but she is not seeing things clearly at the start of the film, and there is no one around who is seeing things clearly. But by the end of the movie she's become a really sharp businesswoman.

Controller: Joy eventually meets an executive at a TV home shopping network who becomes somewhat of a mentor to her, though not as central to the plot as was

Proximo in *Gladiator*. The executive, Neil Walker (played by handsome Bradley Cooper), inspires and instructs Joy about marketing her product on television. Walker is the controller in *Joy*. He directs her in selling her mops just as Ed Harris directed Tom Hanks in flying to the moon.

Input: Neil Walker instructs Joy to "be herself" when she appears on the television home shopping network. He doesn't tell her exactly what that means, but he inspires her to figure it out for herself and trust her instincts.

Transport: Since it's a film about making and selling mops, the director had to be creative in order to depict this in a kinetic, cinematic manner. It must have demanded rather more imagination than filming either a rocket taking off or a swordfight in a Roman arena. The film also uses the musical soundtrack in order to bring movement onto the screen. Mop manufacturing is accompanied by loud rock and roll.

Conversion: When Joy successfully markets her mop on television, the effect of the scene within the context of the movie is the same as Maximus fighting in the arena or Jim Lovell descending to Earth in a fiery re-entry vehicle. It's the culmination of everything that's happened up to that point. A similar effect is achieved at the end of the film when Joy confronts the crooked businessman in Texas who has tried to defraud her. But by then Jennifer Lawrence doesn't have to do anything to express Conversion except calmly look out of a window.

Structure: The action of Joy – family members yelling at each other, mops being made, mops being sold on television – takes place within convincingly rendered environments of squalor and sleaze. A stuffed fish on the wall of an unscrupulous, low-level businessman. A messy basement. A K-Mart parking lot. The structure of the film is decidedly unromantic or unglamorous. But the message is still that magic can happen here. You may not fall in love, but that's not what you really want anyway. You can make a lot of money.

Output: Joy's inner and outer goals are attained, and without the tragic conclusion of *Gladiator* or the bittersweet ending of *Apollo 13*. Joy is rich, and if she's emotionally alone not much attention is paid to that. She's also generous. When entrepreneurs like her former self appear in her office, she's glad to help them out. She's reached a high level of consciousness not just because she's succeeded, but because she's worked through all the Disturbances that arose without becoming corrupted.

VOLUME 2

Your Body Your System

Beyond Diets. How To Achieve Optimal Health
For The Unique <u>YOU</u> in a Dynamic World

INTRODUCTION

"The wisdom of the East" is big business in America. There are probably more yoga studios in Santa Monica than in all of India, and meditation has become so popular, you can even get your mantra online and start today. You can also do both yoga and meditate at the same time. As the famous slogan says, "Just do it!"

The problem is, the American way of yoga and meditation are out of sync with the real meaning of these practices. We're putting the cart before the horse. In traditional times, instruction in yoga and meditation came only after years of service with a guru or teacher. Students had to prove that they could work hard, that they could serve, that they were honorable and worthy human beings. Once that long initiation process was complete, they could be taught yoga and meditation in a few hours. It was the end, not the means to an end.

The real purpose of yoga and meditation is not just to execute difficult poses or get calmed down after a hard day. The purpose is to create awareness and connection with a *system* that includes every aspect of yourself -- and that system extends to encompass the whole world and even the infinite universe.

A simple yoga pose, for example, creates a slight physical stress that influences the act of inhaling a breath, The student learns that there's a connection between the position of your body and how you breathe, That's the start of understanding the system of your body. Similarly, in meditation a conscious relationship is established between awareness of breathing and the flow of thought. Two activities that had seemed disconnected are revealed as parts of an organic system.

And that's only the beginning. Just as breath and thought are elements of your body's system, your body is also an element of a much larger system that literally includes everything. If taken to heart, an insight like that is of much greater value than just putting your foot behind your head. In fact, putting your foot behind your head can actually be a self-centered distraction if the physical act becomes an end in itself.

This book will show how your body can be a laboratory for understanding the system that underlies it --- leading to an intimate understanding of ALL systems in the universe. Further, you'll learn to use that understanding as a gateway to grasping what physicists call "the science of everything." And it's not just theory. It's practical information that will improve your life in mind, body, and spirit.

If you want to simply keep going to yoga classes, find your next "guru," or get on with the latest diet, this book is not for you. If you want a lot more than that -- if you want to learn principles of systems science spanning

162

many millennia to help you discover how your body really operates, in order to get the optimal health you need and deserve -- then this book is for you.

Your Body, Your System presents the fullest explanation of the model of human life as described by the Indian wisdom traditions of Siddha and Ayurveda. The book then connects that traditional model with contemporary systems theory in order to show, first, the holistic, non-reductionist perspective that Siddha and Ayurveda share, and secondly to display the shared content of the old and the new. The book offers some down-to-earth tactics for making a commitment to journey to health in the largest sense of the word -- and for sustaining that commitment with resilience regardless of whatever disturbances arise. Because disturbances will arise.

As you will learn, real health emerges when four conditions have been met. First, you must know what kind of unique system you are --- your *natural system state*, Second, you must recognize optimal health is achieved when you set a goal of maintaining your natural system state. Third, you must become aware of the disturbances that are always arising in the dynamic world around you --- disturbances that can bring deviations from your natural system state. Fourth and last, you must return to your natural system state by making the necessary adjustments to nature's forces.

Health, as this book emphasizes, has nothing to do with "perfection." That's a myth created by "gurus" and diet experts to dupe you into subservience to some reductionist model of health that is neither sustainable nor successful over the long-term. Instead, health is about commitment to a goal, and making ongoing adjustments to achieve that goal. It's a kind of alchemy, in which the forces of nature are manipulated using both art and science. This book will teach you about those forces and the dynamics of all systems, so you can be the master alchemist of the forces inside you.

This book is a part of the Systems Health® series. The foundational science of core principles used in this book are detailed in *The Science of Everything*. In *The System and Revolution*, I provide a systems approach to understand the meaning of revolution, and to expose some of myths of modern science that subvert rational thinking. *Your System, Your Life* focuses on using systems principles to not just support your health but to use the "science of everything" to achieve any goal in life.

My personal background, detailed in Part One, *Journey to Systems*, will provide you with confidence in my ability to be your guide on this journey to a systems-based approach to health. From my birth, I was exposed to *systems* --- systems of oppression as well as systems of truth. My journey to understand the nature of those systems led me to four degrees from MIT, including my PhD in systems biology. This was a journey -- motivated in many ways by something beyond conscious choice --- is at the heart of my work as a scientist, inventor, and revolutionary.

I say "revolutionary" because my intent is to destroy those long-standing systems of oppression, and to create or rediscover those systems that bring truth, freedom and health. In my other books, I include the contents of Part One as a core module in order to provide you insights of how the path I traversed directly motivated my fascination with systems. If you've read it before, you can skip to Part Two.

Being critically aware of the realities of the fundamental weaknesses of the current approaches to health and well being is important on this journey. Part Two provides you that critical awareness. As a Western MIT-trained who was also exposed to Eastern systems of traditional medicine and philosophy at an early age, I will demonstrate how reductionism -- which emphasizes the parts of a system rather than the whole -- is the source of problems not only in Western healthcare, but also of the growing yoga, New Age and meditation movements that claims to be "holistic."

Part Three will present a detailed description of the human system according to Siddha, the 5000 year old Indian wisdom tradition in which I was raised. Part Four then looks at the same issues from the viewpoint of modern systems theory. Both these systems are extremely comprehensive. They share a holistic view of life that transcends reductionist limitations.

Part Five offers practical applications for using a systems-based approach to improve your life, both today and over the long term.

My current work is on developing Systems Health and CytoSolve as entrepreneurial efforts. CytoSolve streamlines the innovation of new drugs by creating computational models of disease and complex biomolecular phenomena. This translates into billions of dollars in savings for American consumers. It will also entirely eliminate the brutal processes of animal testing.

Systems Health integrates East and West to reveal the Science of Everything. This will provide foundational science through which anyone will be able to understand the fundamental principles that run every system in the universe --- whether it's your body, your car, your business, or the workings of a human cell.

As I continue to innovate, I'm confident my current work will be as revolutionary as email, if not more so. That's an ambitious agenda and I'm certain it can be achieved using the principles you'll learn in this book.

Those principles will open your eyes to the interconnections of matter and energy as described by modern systems theory – and, remarkably enough, by Siddha, which originated in India 5000 years. With the same principles that my grandmother employed to make an accurate clinical diagnosis just by looking at someone's face, you will gain insight into the true nature your being and of all humankind as well.

Let's get started….

PART 1

The Journey to Systems

CHAPTER 1

A Child of Oppression and Truth

Like most people, when I look back on my life I see things that seem obvious now, but were invisible when they were actually taking place. I see connections that were waiting to be recognized, but I had to learn to see and understand them.

I have a Ph.D. in systems biology from MIT, for example, but long before I studied the science of systems theory, I had already experienced the presence and power of systems throughout my life. Later in this book you'll learn much more about what systems are and what they can do. But for now, I'll just say that I was born into the caste system of India, I was also introduced as a child to the Indian system of medicine and its wisdom tradition known as Siddha, and later I spent a good amount of time in the caste system of American academia, business, and entertainment.

And, in 1978, I built the first email system and later had to endure the rage, collusion, and deplorable vitriol, starting in 2012 after my work was received by the Smithsonian, of those who sought to destroy me for my daring to assert my rightful place in history as the inventor of email. The truth of a 14-year-old, Indian immigrant boy inventing email in Newark, New Jersey was antagonistic to the priesthood of vested interests, "historians," and "internet pioneers" who wished to perpetuate their gated and well-defined caste system of when, where and by whom innovation could take place.

All of this, of course, has made the study of systems a major focus of my life and work -- but if someone were to ask me what conclusions I've come to regarding my experience with systems, I would have to say I have mixed feelings.

I have certainly seen the limiting and destructive effects of the Indian caste system, and also of the surprisingly similar system that exists in America. In fact, I want to do everything I can to reveal those systems for what they are and destroy them if possible. Yes, destroy them. If that sounds like a radical aspiration, that's exactly what I intend.

On the other hand, I have also seen how Siddha --- another system --- a 5,000 year old system of healing and spirituality, had enormous benefits both for both the physical well being and the spiritual health of the community. Watching my grandmother, who was a Siddha healer, was one of the most important experiences of my life. It showed me the practical benefits and spiritual wisdom that could exist in a system that pre-dated Western science by many centuries. It further showed me that none of this depended on the conventional educational system, and definitely not on academic degrees. When I returned to India years later, I also realized how Siddha anticipated many of the elements of modern systems theory. The terminology was different, but the principles were the same.

There will be much more to say about all this throughout the book. But to begin, I was born in Bombay (now called Mumbai), a cosmopolitan and diverse metropolis with the largest population of any city in India. But I also spent large amounts of time in a small village called Muhavur where my grandparents lived. My grandparents were very small family subsistence farmers --- they tilled the Indian soil growing cotton, coconuts, peanuts and rice.

My grandmother worked in the fields for sixteen hours a day. As I've said, she was also a healer in the traditional Indian system of health called Siddha. This is one of the world's oldest healing systems, and it also anticipates and uses the modern systems approach that you'll learn about in a later chapter.

She could predict what was going on in a person's body simply by looking at that person's face. This skill or art is known in the ancient Indian Tamil treatises as *Samudkrika Lakshanam*. After she diagnosed someone, she could provide a healing modality -- it could include massage, or yoga, or a variety of herbs -- always in sync with the person's specific needs and identity. And that, by the way, is the direction that Western science is now trying to take. It's called *personalized medicine* or *precision medicine* --- giving the right treatment, at the right time, for the right person.

170

My understanding of the knowledge of Siddha and its teachers, known as Siddhars, began by observing my grandmother. Each morning, my grandmother, Chinnathai, would rise before sunrise and, following an ancient tradition, create beautiful drawings known as *kolams* on the ground in front of the entrance to the house. She used milled white rice flour that flowed through her hands, like sand passing through an hourglass, to make abstract geometric and symmetric designs, resembling mandalas.

The kolams served a dual purpose: The rice flour attracted ants and other insects and kept them from entering the home, but there was always a larger, more important, spiritual benefit for the artist and the viewer. Sometimes I would wake up early just to watch my grandmother drawing the daily kolam, a process that was indescribable, with visions emanating from her mind's eye onto the red brown earth. The designs were said to evoke the spiritual world and put one who looked upon them into higher states of consciousness.

Coming home, the kolams were reminders that one was entering a special place. Two solid teak doors were the entrance into a small 10-foot by 12-foot space, which served as the living room, dining room, and the first floor sleeping room. Ahead, one could see the kitchen, where something was always cooking. The fragrance of cumin, ginger, cardamom, red pepper, and freshly ground coconut filled the air. Pictures of the great deities and heroes lined the edge of where the four walls met the ceiling of the living room.

A powerful image of Shiva, my namesake, with the power to destroy, create, and transform; Rama, the virtuous and noble hero of the Ramayana; Devi, the mother Goddess; Parvathi, wife, loyal and devoted consort of Shiva; Ganesha, the elephant headed one who removed obstacles; Jesus, God's avatar and the Savior of mankind; Saraswati, the Goddess of knowledge; Lakshmi, the Goddess of wealth and others. The smell of subtle incense and holy ash was always in the air. My favorite was the deity Muruga, whose picture graced the small altar. Muruga was known as the teacher of teachers or yogi of yogis; the deity's familiar mount was the peacock and above the picture hung a beautiful single peacock feather.

My grandmother knew the ancient arts and was known to be clairvoyant; on occasion she would channel spirits. She had knowledge of the great herbs and medicines to be used for nearly any ailment, and would do rituals and mantras to heal those who requested. Her arms were marked with amazing tattoos. She had a nose ring. Her hair was pitch black and she chewed tobacco and betel leaf. Her face was like the earth, dark with hues of red, and eyes that extended to the beyond, and lines marking her journey across many life times. I thought everyone had a grandmother like her.

She had grown up in Burma, the land of cobras and Buddhism. After giving birth to my father, she did not have another child, something which, at the time, was seen as heresy. There was serious talk of marrying another woman to my grandfather. She and my dad, then five years old, made pilgrimages to many Buddhist

172

temples seeking blessings. One monk with a face my father describes as "pure light," gave my father a mantra, a sacred sound, initiating him to meditation, along with a gold Burmese coin, and a promise that on December 2, he would have a brother. My Uncle Siva was born exactly as predicted and to this day wears that Burmese coin as an amulet. My grandmother then went on to have six other children.

My great-grandfather, who I remember well, was also a hardworking farmer and was considered by local villagers also as a Swamiji, a spiritual Master or Adept, who could perform what we in the West would consider superhuman feats. He was her teacher and trained her in many of the ancient arts. My grandmother had a profound understanding of the power of observation and its ability to reveal Nature's hidden secrets. From her, I learned that all things in Nature are interconnected, and that our intentions are the source of our liberation or bondage.

Every day people would come to her house, asking for healing help; on weekends, long lines extended from her door. No one was refused; no payment was ever required. This was not her occupation; her "day job" was working in the rice and cotton fields to make ends meet. My grandmother often talked to me about healing. She said to heal people one had to have the attitude of a warrior with a desire to serve; she said that being able to serve others was a gift from God.

She was the youngest of sixteen children—the only daughter—and the last remaining member of her family; all her siblings had died. She adored her father, who she described as Robin Hood. He literally stole from the rich and gave to the poor, and was beloved by all. She loved to tell me stories of him and the great epics of Indian lore, of Gods and Demons, good and evil, how virtue and honor always overcame deceit and control.

Gossip was never allowed in her home. At night, she would have me lay my head in her lap and tell me those ancient epic stories. I would always ask her what they meant. She would counsel me gently of the age-old truths of being true, kind, courageous and standing up for those who were less fortunate, reminding me that we are Spirit, and the more we were good, the more God's light would shine through our eyes and face.

She would tell me stories about the great Rama, who fought the evil Ravana, who had stolen Sita his beloved wife. Rama was bold and fought with honor, finally overcoming Ravana and bringing back his wife home to safety. That great epic of the *Ramayana*, the valiant journey of Rama, embedded in me a grand and uncompromising idealism for making the world a better place.

Living in Mumbai I was also exposed to the deplorable realities of India's caste system. My earliest memories, as a five-year-old, was realizing that we were "untouchables" --- low castes.

After playing soccer, I remember going to a nearby house with a friend to get some water. I was asked to stand outside, not allowed to enter, and given water in a markedly different kind of cup --- not the normal silverware. I later asked my mom what this meant. She said that we were low castes, and the home was that of an upper caste, and such segregation was how it was in India.

She shared with me how when she went to get water at the village well --- the upper caste would yell out to her as though she was a dirty animal and say, "shoo, shoo Shudra." The word "Shudra" is as derogatory and demeaning as the word "Nigger." She was only allowed to get water when they were not there.

So, as a child I wanted to understand not only the systems of ancient medicine my grandmother practiced to heal others but also the larger systems of oppression such as the caste system, and how to overcome and destroy it to bring truth, freedom and health to the world. Quite an ambition for a young child.

CHAPTER 2

The Invention of Email

It was these multiple worlds of Mumbai and Muhavur that I was exposed to during my formative years --- and it was that world I took with me when in 1970 my family emigrated from India to New Jersey, on my seventh birthday.

My parents made this move for two reasons. First, we were considered, as I shared, "untouchables" in the Indian caste system, and, in spite of their incredible capabilities and achievements as low-caste Indians, they had hit a ceiling for advancement in India -- and secondly, they wanted to find better educational opportunities for their kids --- my sister and me.

However, 1970 was not a good year economically in America. There was a recession underway and the original job my father had been offered in Chicago didn't work out as the recession had caused layoffs and job reductions. So, we moved first to Paterson, New Jersey, one of the poorest cities in the country, where my dad found an alternate job.

During my early years in New Jersey, I was certainly encouraged to do well in school, but I was also very much into sports. I wasn't the typical nerd. I was into baseball and soccer -- but I completed all the school's math courses, including Calculus, by the ninth grade, and even published a paper in a mathematics journal as a teenager. I did well in school for a very specific reason. I had been inspired by my grandmother and I wanted to learn medicine and healing. I had very practical goals.

At that time in 1977, the Courant Institute for Mathematical Science at NYU had started a new innovative program in which only forty young students were invited to come to NYU to study an intensive program in Computer Science --- an emerging field as computers themselves were very new.

This program was created by a visionary professor named Henry Mullish. He saw that software programming would one day be a primary need in the high tech revolution that was just beginning, and the United States would need software engineers. I was one of the forty students selected, and I learned eight programming languages at NYU. It was a twelve hour per day program and it went on for over two months. I was the only Indian in the program, and I was also the youngest student. I finished number one in the class.

Getting to NYU from New Jersey involved taking buses and trains, starting at around five in the morning. I'd arrive in New York around seven, and then walk to the University through the colorful and sometimes threatening environment that was New York in those days.

When the NYU program finished, I was very bored by the idea of going back to high school. I was even thinking about dropping out. Fortunately my mom had gotten a degree in statistics in India at a time when it was very unusual, or even revolutionary, for a woman to do anything like that. She was working as a systems analyst at a small, three-campus medical school called the University of Medicine and Dentistry of New Jersey (UMDNJ). Her job was located at the Newark campus of UMDNJ.

My mother introduced me to a scientist named Dr. Swamy Laxminarayan who had a large amount of data on the sudden crib death of infants in their sleep --- also known as SIDS. He asked me to explore the data using artificial intelligence and pattern analysis techniques to see if there was a correlation between infants' sleep patterns and crib death. I developed computer software algorithms to find such correlations. This was my introduction to AI and pattern analysis of what we today call "big data."

The results of my study were later published as a scientific paper at a major medical conference in Finland. This was very exciting and gratifying for me, since it was directly connected to my interest in medicine and healing. I was on my chosen path.

It turned out, however, that my ability to program the computer and work on sleep patterns had attracted the attention of another visionary scientist. His name was Dr. Leslie P. Michelson, and he was a brilliant PhD

178

in experimental particle physics from Brookhaven Labs who was now at UMDNJ. Dr. Michelson had created the Laboratory Computer Network (LCN) which connected the three campuses of Newark, Piscataway and New Brunswick, in New Jersey. This network had nothing to do with the ARPANET or internet, etc. It was an independent network.

Dr. Michelson was also developing new scientific computing software applications to support research at UMDNJ. He had set high standards for any software that was created in his small computer lab at UMDNJ. It had to be bulletproof -- which meant it had to be highly reliable -- and it also had to be user friendly. I was only fourteen years old, but Dr. Michelson didn't treat me like a child. He wanted to challenge me. He wanted to push me as far as I could go.

Dr. Michelson told me about the interoffice mail system that was then used at UMDNJ, and was also used all over the country. He then challenged me to create software that would literally be an electronic replacement for the interoffice paper mail system that connected approximately one thousand offices at the three campuses of UMDNJ. The system I built included an Inbox, Outbox, Drafts, Folders, Memo, Attachments, Carbon Copies (including Blind Carbon Copies), Return Receipt, Address Book, Groups, Forward, Compose, Edit, Reply, Delete, Archive, Sort, and Bulk Distribution. I accomplished this task by writing nearly 50,000 lines of computer code across a system of 35 computer programs which I named "email" -- a term never before used in the English language. It was not a simple system, but a sophisticated enterprise class system.

It worked, was successful, and was used across the university. I wrote a user's manual, held user training sessions and maintained the system by fixing issues and adding new features --- all of this while finishing up some remaining courses in high school.

This whole experience was certainly a major turning point in my life. Creating a major invention like email was of course important. But even at the time I was aware that Dr. Michelson's giving me this assignment represented a complete and total rejection of any caste system -- yes, even in America -- based on age, race, or nationality. He opened the gates for me --- where a 14-year-old boy was invited to work alongside those who were three to five decades older, in a collegial environment, where I was treated no less, with the only expectation being that my work, the product of my labor, would be the judge of my stature --- nothing else.

This was freedom in the interests of science and innovation, and nothing else mattered. I wish I could say that everyone I've encountered in years since then has been as free from prejudice as Leslie Michelson, but that hasn't been the case. As a result, my work has often involved not only a search for innovation, but for justice as well.

At that time, in terms of electronic communication, earlier work had been done on sending rudimentary text messages between computers. But I want to emphasize that email was not just exchanging text messages. Email is a *system* with many interconnected parts that would enable collaboration in the electronic world as the interoffice mail system did in the world of paper and the physical world. Email was a full replica of the secretary's desktop along with all the communication features needed to transact business in an office environment.

Subsequently I won a Westinghouse Science Honors Award for creating email, and I was accepted at MIT. In fact, when I first arrived at MIT, the front page of the MIT newspaper featured three of the 1,041 incoming students' work, and I was one of them for having created email.

Email became something I had done in the past, I didn't focus on it, but I didn't entirely forget about it either. Upon attending MIT, in September of 1981, I learned from the MIT President Dr. Paul E. Gray during dinner at his home that the Supreme Court was not recognizing software patents; however, he advised me to Copyright my invention, since the recent Computer Software Act of 1980 allowed inventors to protect their software inventions using Copyright. That is what I did.

On August 30, 1982, the United States government awarded me the first U.S. Copyright for "Email." I want to emphasize this Copyright was significant since the Supreme Court was not yet recognizing software patents --- a Copyright was the only way to protect software inventions. Therefore, to the greatest extent possible at the time, I was officially recognized as the inventor of email by the United States government.

This sequence of events could have developed very differently if government policies regarding patents had not lagged behind the pace of innovation. Had I been allowed to patent email, I'd now be receiving a penny for every transmission and I'd be a gazillionaire.

CHAPTER 3

Somethings Need to Be Destroyed

Over the next thirty years I sought neither recognition nor financial gain for my invention of email. At MIT I earned four degrees in engineering and design, including a PhD in biological engineering. I was also interested in political systems, since I wanted answers to the oppressive caste system my family and I had experienced in India. I had the opportunity to study with Noam Chomsky, who is both the father of modern linguistics and also one of the most outspoken political thinkers in academia. I learned why and how the Indian caste system came into being --- a historical set of events that very few Indians are even aware of.

During my years at MIT, I always pursued entrepreneurial projects. I was in and out of the university, getting a degree, then leaving to start a company, then getting another degree --- one foot in academia, and one foot out.

By 1993, with the advent of the World Wide Web, email went from being a business application to becoming the dominant form of communication in all fields. At that time, I was doing my PhD in developing a universal AI and pattern analysis system for all sorts of media, including document content, handwriting analysis, and speech signals. During this time, the Clinton White House ran a competition to find an AI solution to their problem of email overload.

The White House had twenty interns sorting 5,000 emails a day into 147 predefined categories including education, healthcare, and many more. Each incoming email would be categorized into one of the categories, and then the sender would receive a form letter associated with a category. It was a very time consuming process. In an attempt to bring this situation under control, the government announced the competition for analyzing and sorting the emails. No such thing had ever been done before, because there had been no need for anything like this.

I entered the competition as the only graduate student. The other entrants were five public and private companies. I won and was selected to provide the service.

Out of that experience I started a company called EchoMail, which helped major corporations process large volumes of email from clients and customers. I thought EchoMail would be a two year project. However, it became a ten year enterprise with 300 employees, and I grew it to $250 million in value. I personally made a lot of money.

In the midst of this, in 2003, my advisor called and urged me come back to MIT to finish my PhD. A major global science initiative, called the Human Genome Project, had just ended which mapped the entire human genome. Despite what the scientists had expected, it turned out that human beings have approximately the same number of genes as an earthworm --- about 20,000. In this atmosphere, the field of *systems biology* was coming into its own, saying we needed to look beyond genes as the "answer to everything." We needed to see the interconnections of molecules across the genome and their communication in cells, just as my grandmother had seen how the facial features of someone connected to their bodily functions.

At this time the National Science Foundation (NSF) had issued what they called the "Grand Challenge," comparable to landing on the moon. The challenge was to mathematically model the whole human cell. I returned to MIT and combined my love of computers with my devotion to medicine and created the technology of CytoSolve in response to the NSF challenge. If Email was the electronic version of the interoffice mail communication system, CytoSolve was the electronic version of the molecular communication system. This could mean the final elimination of animal testing in laboratories.

Based on my work on CytoSolve, MIT awarded me a PhD. In that same year in 2007 I received a Fulbright Fellowship to return to India to study Siddha from a systems biology perspective. The front page of MIT's official newspaper, *MIT Tech Talk*, headlined a feature article: "East meets West: Armed with 4 MIT degrees, Shiva Ayyadurai embarks on new adventure."

This had been my childhood aspiration to understand scientifically how my grandmother was able to heal others using Siddha. My training in systems biology at MIT provided me all the necessary skills.

I discovered that the Siddhars had always been systems thinkers. Unlike conventional Western medicine, they were not reductionist. They didn't look at people and their health in a fragmented way. Their view of health was genuinely holistic.

I discovered a common language, a science, that connected Siddha with modern control systems theory. This was a major breakthrough, and would become the basis of my future teaching and curriculum on Systems Health and "The Science of Everything."

On the night before I was set to leave India to return to the US, following completion of my Fulbright research in 2009, I was called to a meeting with the Director General of the Council of Scientific and Industrial Research (CSIR). CSIR was India's largest scientific enterprise comprised of 37 labs across India and over 4,500 scientists. He invited me to serve as the head of the CSIR's new initiative, "CSIR-TECH," to spin out scientific innovations -- innovations that had just been sitting in the lab -- to the general population of India. The idea was to expedite the transition from the lab bench to the masses.

In this role, I developed a strategic plan for unleashing innovation from those labs by implementing an entrepreneurial program. I visited nearly 1,500 CSIR

Indian scientists all over the country and met people who were absolutely brilliant. Amazing innovations were being developed. But these innovations were being sidetracked by administrators and bureaucrats who were jealous and afraid. There was a high level of corruption.

I wrote an honest report in October of 2009 that exposed the sycophancy, corruption and suppression that was taking place in Indian science. Within hours, I was fired, and was later evicted from my home. Death threats followed, and also threats from the Director General to reporters of major papers: they were not to share the facts. I was forced to flee India on a dramatic journey that included a 32-hour train ride to the Nepal border, plane flight to Kathmandu, and three other airplane flights before I was finally back home in Boston.

Prior to my dismissal, I had been awarded the First Outstanding Scientist/Technologist of Indian Origin by the Prime Minister of India, who serves as the President of CSIR. I had been appointed as Additional Secretary in the Indian government, with the highest Scientist Level H posting. Major newspapers, including *The New York Times*, covered the events of my dismissal, in spite of threats from the Director General of CSIR against NY Times reporters. I was commissioned to write an article for *Nature* by the Nature India editor, which I entitled "Innovation Demands Freedom." Shortly after this article was published, the editor of Nature India was threatened by the then Prime Minister's Office, and the article was removed.

Sometime after I returned to Boston, in late 2011, my mother was dying of pulmonary fibrosis. Much to my surprise, she presented me with a suitcase filled with all the artifacts of my early work on email from 1978 -- my fifty thousand lines of code, everything.

One of my colleagues, a professor at Emerson College reviewed the materials and said, "Shiva, you invented email." As I reviewed the materials, I could, however, only think back to the amazing collegial ecosystem at UMDNJ which allowed a 14-year-old boy to innovate and invent email --- far different than the oppressive and draconian feudal system of CSIR in India, which suppressed innovation.

My friend contacted Doug Aamoth, who was the Technology Editor at *Time Magazine*. Doug reviewed the materials carefully over many weeks and wrote a feature article entitled "The Man Who Invented Email," which informed the general public about email's true origin. In 2012, the Smithsonian Institution's National Museum of American History (NMAH) requested and received the artifacts that documented my work, which really did epitomize the American Dream.

On February 16, 2012, an event was held at the Smithsonian to celebrate the acquisition of all that material. It was after that ceremony that controversy began, which is extensively documented on the Internet. The "controversy" was incited by a group calling itself a "special interest group" body of "computer historians" --- these were industry insiders, loyal to the major defense contractor Raytheon/BBN, who had falsely crowned one of its own employees as the "inventor of email."

After three decades of not promoting my work, these people attacked me as if I were a money-hungry

188

opportunist. The online gossip site Gizmodo called me an "asshole," "a dick," and "a fraud." These inspired threats on other blogs that "the curry-stained Indian should be shot and hanged by his dhothi," and expletives such as "nigger Indian."

Why were there such vicious attacks against me? The reason is simple. The idea that a 14-year-old immigrant Indian boy working in an obscure hospital could invent email disrupted the carefully nurtured storyline that major innovations always had to come from the triangle of big corporations, major universities and the military --- what President Eisenhower and Senator Fulbright had referred to as the "military-industrial-academic" complex.

Specifically, concerning email, those innovations had to come from defense contractors. Therefore those defense contractors should receive whatever huge funding they wanted, because so many wonderful things like email came out of that -- which in actuality had not come from military initiatives.

But the facts on who invented email are black and white. There never was a genuine controversy. The whole media storm was fabricated to continue brainwashing Americans with the idea that innovations come from war, and we as Americans should be happy funding war since we get Tang and Velcro --- which by the way also didn't come from military research either.

The attacks on my reputation were libelous and defamatory. However, I was not able to find an attorney to take on this Goliath of an enemy.

In 2016, after four years of attempting to find an attorney, I signed with Charles Harder, who represented the ex-pro wrestler Hulk Hogan in a highly publicized case against Gawker Media. Charles Harder filed a suit against Gawker Media and I was victorious.

On November 3, 2016 Gawker Media settled with me for $750,000 and removed all three defamatory online articles. This was a big victory for the inventor of email, and more importantly it established the truth that innovation, small or large, can occur anytime, anyplace, by anybody.

Immediately after this victory, the response from the defeated cabal of vested interests was exactly what would be expected: a desire for revenge. This was expressed by frantic blog posts stating that "Shiva Ayyadurai didn't invent email."

Their belief seemed to be that, if they said it loud enough, that untruth would become fact. This is a familiar tactic of those in power: repeat a lie loud and long in order to brainwash the masses.

As this false storyline was being created, the establishment cabal then colluded together to further libel and defame me on the very influential Wikipedia site. Within weeks of my legal victory, the cabal rewrote the opening sentences of my Wikipedia page, -- which would be the first item on a Google search -- stating that the only notable achievement of my life was to have created a controversy by asserting myself as the inventor of email.

But in fact there was no longer any controversy, if there ever had been one. The fact is that I had won and that win would be recognized by a payment of $750,000 from the people who had libeled me in contradiction of the facts.

The defamatory articles were removed because the business folks at Gawker Media and Univision did not want to suffer even greater damage to their wallets. Money, in an odd way, can sometimes motivate justice.

My experiences have brought renewed knowledge of how systems work, and that knowledge will be most powerful weapon to destroy whatever systems oppress the broad mass of humanity. At that same time, that knowledge will provide the insight to create and embrace systems that bring us truth, freedom and health --- as did the Siddha system that my grandmother practiced, without any college degrees.

My core mission, in this book and everywhere else, is to bring you an understanding of systems theory and practice. With that understanding, you will see for yourself that truth is an emergent property arising from the interconnections of the components of any system.

Email, therefore, is not a simple exchange of text messages, but a system which emerges from the interconnection of the many components originally resident in the interoffice mail system. Health emerges from complex, dynamic combinations biological elements -- not from one "magic bullet" drug, or diet, or exercise.

In a similar way, real freedom will not emerge from fighting one aspect of the enemy, whether it's racism, sexism, or classism. Freedom will come from defeating the priesthood system of academia, media, politics, and even entertainment that keeps humanity in bondage through a complex interaction of oppression. The ultimate goal of that system is to dehumanize the many by asserting that only the few are innovative, intelligent, beautiful, and all-knowing.

For the great Siddhars, the revolutionaries, the warriors, the heart of their struggle was against these priesthoods and their caste system. Some things do need to be destroyed --- and that caste system is one such thing.

PART 2

Reductionism: West & East

CHAPTER 4

Western Medicine. Wartime Medicine

An essential purpose of this book is to present an integrative, genuinely holistic perspective on health and the human body. That's how the body was understood by the ancient wisdom traditions, and that's how it is now understood by modern systems theory.

Enlightened healers in both the past and the present have recognized the fundamental interconnectedness of the human system. To advanced thinkers in any period, it's always been clear that the correct way to understand something -- especially something as complex as the human body -- is not to "take it apart" either literally or figuratively.

Yet taking things apart has been the basis of much of Western science for hundreds of years. Needless to say, science has brought us immense benefits. But it has also failed to solve some key problems, and sometimes has even made them worse.

194

The modern healthcare system as currently practiced in the United States and throughout the Western world faces serious challenges. These include high costs, inconsistent quality of care, and a drug development process that is extremely inefficient, expensive, and sometimes dangerous.

Reductionism enabled a healthcare system that was able to respond effectively to acute crises but was ineffective in meeting the growing demand for prevention. Yet only prevention brings about genuine well being and not just a suppression of symptoms, and is considerate of the long-term effects of particular therapeutics, protocols and procedures.

The modern healthcare system was born during the Industrial Revolution, beginning in the late 18th century, and was structured to manage the emergencies of war. Our present system was originally designed to handle life and death crises on the battlefield, needing immediate and reactive solutions. Battlefield "healthcare" demanded a reductionist philosophy.

Those conditions compelled a reductionist thinking.

Wartime situations demanded healthcare that rewarded specialization and "magic bullet" solutions, which triaged to a single drug, the right specialist, or the right procedure to address immediate and catastrophic events. Reductionism was effective for these critical situations, delivering life-saving solutions drugs and surgical techniques to solve problems – but generally after the onset of wound, a disease, or the effects of a natural disaster.

In line with its origins, reductionism continues to pervade basic research, patient treatment and drug development. This compels increasing specialization, where a problem is divided into to many smaller problems. These smaller problems are then assigned to individuals with even greater specialization. This has resulted in a system with an increasing number of disconnected parts and disconnected solutions. New drugs, new protocols, and new technologies enable control over ever smaller and more specialized processes.

For clinical problems such as Alzheimer's, diabetes, or cancer, for example, this paradigm of research isolates small pieces of the problem and studies them out of context. As a result, solutions are provided that may be ineffective for the patient as a whole being.

The skyrocketing costs of care are a direct result of such failure. Currently, the percentage of US GDP for health care is approximately 5%, while defense spending was approximately 4% of US GDP in 2013. By 2050, however, healthcare costs are projected to double to 10% of GDP, while defense spending is expected to remain at 4%. These rising costs are not delivering a concomitant improvement in quality of care.

In the United Kingdom, for example, one in five patients suffer harm caused *after* admission into National Health Services hospitals. In the United States, the statistics are even more startling. One in three hospital patients experience adverse events and about 7% of these patients are harmed permanently or die as a result, according to a 2010 study. This is a far higher rate than shown an earlier study, in which the rate was one in four for Medicare patients during a hospital stay.

If the US transportation system delivered equivalent results, with one in four drivers having some type of accident whenever they took to the roads, it is likely that many people would look for alternative modes of transport.

The high cost of pharmaceuticals is another example of the current system's failure. Upwards of $5 billion are needed to produce a single drug that takes nearly 15 years to develop. The drug development process is an *open loop system*, with minimal feedback. This ineffective system produces drugs that are only effective for a small segment of the target population since they are not personalized, yet they pose significant risks and side effects for the majority. The attempt to address this problem by simply increasing spending on research and development is not working.

As the following chart illustrates, year-by-year increases in research and development actually result in year-over-year *decreases* in new drug approvals --- new molecular entities (NMEs) --- by the US Food and Drug Administration (FDA). Rising costs, stagnant quality of care, and an ineffective drug development process suggest that the root causes of the healthcare systems' reductionist failure have yet to be addressed.

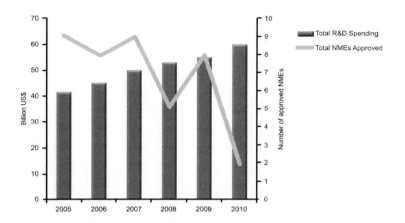

The over-specialization of disciplines that results from this reductionism makes it challenging for a practitioner or researcher to pull together sufficient fundamental knowledge to innovate viable diagnostics or interventions. Moreover, funding and investments in basic science and research do not promote or inspire the interdisciplinary or trans-disciplinary cooperation needed to create significant clinical discoveries and applications.

Reductionist thinking always moves in one direction -- from low order phenomenon to higher order phenomenon -- and ignores the possibility of complex higher order systems exerting a influence on more basic lower order systems. Biogenetic determinism, for example, moves explanation of social and behavioral problems to *just* the genes, where the lone individual, rather than social conditions or economic inequalities, are made responsible.

When people are taught that their genes are the only reason for their illnesses, the results is a sense of

198

helplessness or even guilt. The reductionist approach steers a system that prescribes and develops drugs as the sole method to "solve" problems, whether the problems are social, interpersonal, emotional, or even spiritual

The alternative to reductionism is a systems approach. This is based on a holistic understanding that a system cannot be understood by taking it apart. There is no "magic bullet," since *emergent properties* manifesting as parts of a system interact together. From these interactions, new properties of systems emerge -- properties that could not be predicted from the characteristics of any individual part.

Years of work and study with both modern systems theory and ancient wisdom traditions have taught me several important facts. First, a systems approach toward human life and toward reality in general has been understood in Siddha for many centuries. We'll explore that system in detail in Part Three.

But first it's important to see how Western reductionism has adapted -- or corrupted? -- the powerful traditions of the East for substantial profits. This is in stark contrast to how yoga, for example, was taught and understood in the past -- and how, we hope, it can again be taught and understood in the future.

CHAPTER 5

Modern "Yoga"

The history of yoga extends back thousands of years. Many of the early teachings were passed orally from one generation to another, and did not exist in writing until centuries after their creation. Even when written teachings were brought into being, it's likely that they were transcribed onto palm leaves which of course were far from permanent. Although some researchers believe that yoga may be up to 10,000 years old, this long and rich history can be divided into four main periods of innovation, practice, and development.

Pre-Classical Yoga

The beginnings of yoga emerged in India at least 5,000 years ago. The word yoga was first mentioned in the oldest sacred texts which are collectively known as the Rig Veda. These were an aggregation songs, mantras and rituals to be used by Vedic priests. Yoga was slowly refined and developed by the priests and mystic seers who documented their practices and beliefs in the Upanishads, a huge work containing over 200 scriptures. The most important of the Yogic scriptures is the Bhagavad-Gîtâ, composed around 500 B.C. The Upanishads adapted the concept of ritual sacrifice from the Vedas and spiritualized it, advocating sacrifice of the ego through self-knowledge, positive action, and wisdom (jnana yoga).

Classical Yoga

In the pre-classical stage, yoga was a compendium of ideas, beliefs, and practices that often conflicted or even contradicted each other. The Classical period is generally said to begin with the Yoga-Sûtras of Patanjali, a sage who composed them some time around 400AD. Patanjali organized the practice of yoga into an "eight limbed path" containing the steps and stages towards obtaining Samadhi, or enlightenment. Patanjali is often considered the father of yoga and the Yoga-Sûtras still influence most styles of current practice.

Post-Classical Yoga

In the centuries after Patanjali, yoga masters created a system of health practices designed to rejuvenate the physical body and prolong life. They rejected the teachings of the ancient Vedas and embraced the physical body as the means to achieve enlightenment. Tantra Yoga, for example, was a collection of techniques for cleansing the body and mind to break the bonds that limit our physical existence, and therefore also limit our spiritual potential. This exploration of these physical-spiritual connections and body centered practices led to the creation Hatha Yoga, which has become the primary style of yoga in the West.

The Modern Period

In the late 19th and early 20th centuries, yoga masters began to travel to the West, attracting attention and followers. The 1893 Chicago World's Fair included a Parliament of Religions in which Swami Vivekananda lectured on yoga and the universality of the world's religions. In the 1920s and 30s, Hatha Yoga was strongly promoted in India with the work of T. Krishnamacharya, Swami Sivananda, and other masters of Hatha Yoga.

Krishnamacharya opened the first Hatha Yoga school in Mysore in 1924 and in 1936 Sivananda founded the Divine Life Society on the banks of the Ganges River. Krishnamacharya produced three students that would continue his legacy and increase the popularity of Hatha Yoga: B.K.S. Iyengar, T.K.V. Desikachar and Pattabhi Jois. Sivananda wrote more than 200 books on yoga, and established nine ashrams and numerous yoga centers located around the world.

Selling Yoga Successfully

The importation of yoga in the West gained momentum when Indra Devi opened her yoga studio in Hollywood in 1947. Indra Devi deserves to be more well known than she presently is. Born in Russia, she spent significant amounts of time in India where she took on an Indian-sounding name and was instructed by some yoga masters. Later, in the U.S., she taught yoga to some prominent actresses, inaugurating a connection between celebrities and yoga that remains strong today. Partly as a result of this popularization, Hatha Yoga with its emphasis on postures more than spirituality has gained millions of followers. There is no doubt that yoga practitioners at all levels now outnumber anything in the past by many orders of magnitude.

The health benefits of yoga, both physical and emotional, are now beyond question. A recent article in a Harvard University Health Letter documents this. As the letter explains, by reducing perceived stress and anxiety, yoga appears to modulate stress response systems. This, in turn, decreases physiological arousal by reducing the heart rate, lowering blood pressure, and easing respiration. There is also evidence that yoga practices help increase heart rate variability, an indicator of the body's ability to respond to stress more flexibly.

In 2008, researchers at the University of Utah presented preliminary results from a study of varied participants' responses to pain. They note that people who have a poorly regulated response to stress are also more sensitive to pain. Their subjects were 12 experienced yoga practitioners, 14 people with fibromyalgia -- considered by many researchers to be a stress-related illness characterized by hypersensitivity to pain -- and 16 healthy volunteers.

When the three groups were subjected to more or less painful thumbnail pressure, the participants with fibromyalgia perceived pain at lower pressure levels than the other subjects. Functional MRIs showed they also had the greatest activity in areas of the brain associated with the pain response. In contrast, the yoga practitioners had the highest pain tolerance and lowest pain-related brain activity during the MRI. The study underscores the value of techniques, such as yoga, that can help a person regulate their stress and, therefore, pain responses.

In a German study published in 2005, 24 women who described themselves as "emotionally distressed" took two 90-minute yoga classes a week for three months. Women in a control group maintained their normal activities and were asked not to begin an exercise or stress-reduction program during the study period.

Though not formally diagnosed with depression, all participants had experienced emotional distress for at least half of the previous 90 days. They were also one standard deviation above the population norm in scores for perceived stress (measured by the Cohen Perceived Stress Scale), anxiety (measured using the Spielberger State-Trait Anxiety Inventory), and depression (scored with the Profile of Mood States and the Center for Epidemiological Studies Depression Scale, or CES-D).

At the end of three months, women in the yoga group reported improvements in perceived stress, depression, anxiety, energy, fatigue, and well-being. Depression scores improved by 50%, anxiety scores by 30%, and overall well-being scores by 65%. Initial complaints of headaches, back pain, and poor sleep quality also resolved much more often in the yoga group than in the control group.

A uncontrolled, descriptive study in 2005 examined the effects of a single yoga class for inpatients at a New

Hampshire psychiatric hospital. The 113 participants included patients with bipolar disorder, major depression, and schizophrenia. After the class, average levels of tension, anxiety, depression, anger, hostility, and fatigue dropped significantly, as measured by the Profile of Mood States, a standard 65-item questionnaire that participants answered on their own before and after the class. Patients who chose to participate in additional classes experienced similar short-term positive effects.

Hundreds of other studies attest to the health benefits of yoga, just as many studies document the benefits of aspirin. This is not an insignificant analogy. In the United States yoga, like aspirin, is not only clinically effective but is also a product within the general environment of Western healthcare.

Consequently, and not surprisingly, yoga has now come to be marketed within a modern reductionist framework. As we discussed in the previous chapter, the essence of reductionism is taking things apart and examining the parts separately. This viewpoint is so ingrained in modern thought that it happens almost as a reflex. Regarding yoga, it means abandoning a holistic perspective and selecting yoga styles like items from a salad bar.

The concept of chakras, which exists in several forms of Eastern medicine and spirituality, have proved to be a convenient tool for not integration, but ironically, across East and West, a path towards a reductionist yoga.

CHAPTER 6

Chakras of Reductionism

Chakras are seven points in the body in which channels of energy -- known as nadis -- intersect and intensify. Each chakra regulates a specific category of our physical, emotional, and spiritual being. In the original systems of yoga, an integrative approach provided methods to exercise and unify all seven chakras.

However, commercialized yoga, be it America or India, now has followed a dis-integrated and reductionist path, which asserts that we can select a particular yoga style, or even a specific pose, that will benefit an individual chakra. It's just like taking one pill for a headache and another for an upset stomach. Individual schools and gurus of yoga, now commercialize their particular yoga methods --- marketing and selling them in a competitive capitalist market, attempting to convince you that one form is better than another.

As if it were a business or a corporation, business, they have now segmented yoga into vertical markets: Kundalini Yoga, Hatha Yoga, Kriya Yoga, Bhakti Yoga,

Yoga of Bhajans and Kirtans, Third Eye Meditation, and Surat Shabd Yoga.

My experience across all of these yoga and meditation forms, along with a systems-based perspective, has allowed me recognize that the reductionism in yoga follows the literal dissection of the chakras into different parts.

Root Chakra: Kundalini Yoga

The *root chakra*, or the first chakra, at the base of the spine is the focus of the Kundalini Yoga form. Kundalini Yoga involves activating the root chakra, also known as the *muladhara,* to "uncoil the serpent" at the base of the spine to move the energy upward towards the other six charas, and ultimately to the crown chakra on top of the head. One of my teachers, the late Swami Satyananda was said to be one of the great Kundalini masters.

The proponents of Kundalini promote that this yoga form is the ultimate form, as it focuses on the base of the spine, which is the "root" of the body. The Kundalini form is also associated with Tantra Yoga and sexual prowess. It is said that those who can control their kundalini have also mastered sexual arts.

Sacral Chakra: Hatha Yoga

The form that most Americans associate with "yoga" is Hatha Yoga, with its poses known as asanas. This yoga form primarily focuses on methods that affect the second or *sacral* chakra, also known as the *svadhistana,* located between the pelvic bone and the navel. Yogis of this form emphasize deep stretches, holding poses, and particular contortions to create flexibility and strength.

There are nearly 20 million practitioners of this yoga form in the United States. It comes in a variety of branded identities such as Bikram Yoga, Hot Yoga, Vinyasa Yoga, and others. A multi-billion dollar apparel and fashion industry which has also emerged from Hatha Yoga.

Solar Plexus Chakra: Kriya Yoga and Pranayama

The third chakra, called the *solar plexus chakra*, is located between the navel and the solar plexus. It's also known as *manipura*. Kriya Yoga and Pranayama (breath yoga) are primarily based on energizing this chakra through a variety of "kriyas" and breath work.

Kriyas are a collection of techniques to cleanse and activate the solar plexus chakra. Pranayama uses powerful breathing exercises to enhance digestion and metabolism, which are important functions of the solar plexus chakra. There are entire treatises written on Kriya Yoga as well as the use of different types of pranayamas for supporting this chakra.

Heart Chakra: Bhakti Yoga and Karma Yoga

The *heart chakra*, the fourth chakra, is also known as *anahata*. It is the basis of Bhakti Yoga or Karma Yoga, which focuses on "opening the heart," and employs visualization methods to let love flow through one's entire being by remaining "heart centered." The hippie movement of the early 1960s for peace, love and understanding was influenced by "mystics" of the East who were proponents of the heart centered approach.

The word "devotion" in the Indian language perhaps best describes the essence of Bhakti Yoga. Masters of this yoga form emphasized "nine steps," which included expression of love and devotion through various forms. These included veneration of a master, devotion to the arts, and commitment to a vocation --- or even to one's day-to-day work. Swami Vivekananda was a proponent of both Bhakti Yoga and the closely related Karma Yoga, which emphasizes performing one's work and daily routine with devotion and love in order to "burn off karma."

The Throat Chakra: Bhajans and Kirtans

The fifth, or throat chakra, is also known as vishuddha. Singing and vocal expression through devotional songs known as Bhajans or Kirtans are said to open a gateway of communication to the heavens. The songs are indeed beautiful and expressive --- in some ways much like gospel music in the United States.

Those who have blocked areas of communication within themselves, as well as with others, have found Bhajans and Kirtans very valuable to emotional health and healing. Today a growing number of Western vocal artists who have adopted Indian singing styles to connect with this market. Ravi Shankar and George Harrison were among the earliest East/West duos who brought this to the modern world.

Third-Eye Chakra: Third Eye Meditation

As a child, I was trained by my grandfather and later by Swami Muktananda on meditation to open the sixth chakra, known as the *third eye chakra*, or as *ajna*. This can use a blend of mantras (internal repetition of sounds) while concentrating on a point between the eyebrows to visualize a blue light, or to visualize a goal one would like to achieve.

I have personally found third-eye meditation of enormous value for achieving goals, as well as staying focused on a goal from day to day. Many athletes and successful business people are known to use third-eye meditation.

Crown Chakra: Surat Shabd Yoga

The *sahasara,* or the crown chakra, is located at the top of the head. There are teachers who assert that this seventh chakra is the only one worth focusing on, as it leads to ultimate liberation or *moksha.* Surat Shabd Yoga --- the yoga of the sound current --- focuses on connecting with the crown chakra through sound -- including literal "soul travel" to the ultimate source of creation.

The Radha Soami Society, as well as the Sufis and other mystical schools use variations of Surat Shabd Yoga to perform soul travel and have out of body experiences. I've had my own experiences with this yoga form. Various sounds are said to enable connection with different states of consciousness. Practice involves a combination of contemplation and mantras.

As should be evident from this discussion of the individual chakras and their associated yoga forms, there is no "one" yoga. Yoga has many branches, but this should not translate into a reductionist adherence to a single style. Yet the reductionist marketing of yoga has been hugely successful, to the point where we can now actually speak of an American "yoga industry." But that's something quite different from the original tradition.

The ancient Siddhars were not idealists. They were practical scholars and scientists who respected both the visible and invisible worlds. They believed that it is our duty to take care of our bodies, which they saw as sacred physical vessels. Even if we place a priority on being good souls—pure hearted human beings—we need our physical vessels to help us express our high aspirations.

In this sense both the material body and the invisible body -- a pure heart and good soul -- are essential to human fulfillment. The teachers emphasized exercising all chakras. In order to be a whole human being, one had to:

1) Be sexual (root chakra);

2) Move and be flexible (sacral chakra);

3) Have excellent digestion and process food well (solar plexus chakra);

4) Feel for others and be devoted and compassionate (heart chakra);

5) Sing, communicate and be heard (throat chakra);

6) Set and achieve goals (third-eye chakra); and,

7) connect with spirit (crown chakra)

211

The Siddhars considered it hypocrisy to meditate on a mountain top or do good deeds for others while allowing one's own body to disintegrate. Their entire system emphasized a personal responsibility that was grounded across the worlds of Matter, as well as Energy and Information. About one thing, they were very clear: take care of your physical body at all levels.

The Siddhars were so clear about this that in ancient times, they did not allow students to pursue the stillness practice of meditation -- which primarily supports the realms of Energy and Information -- unless they were physically strong in the worlds of Matter. One had to have the outer strength of a warrior before being allowed to focus on the inner realms and learn the more esoteric practice of meditation.

Indeed, millennia ago the study of Yoga was taught only to warriors. In that tradition, Yoga began with physical exercises, and then moved to more meditative practices--after the physical vessel was made strong and relaxed enough to perform meditation without physical distractions. It's an ironic truth that sitting quietly in silence actually requires great physical strength!

One of my teacher's teachers, the great Sivananda, a Siddha Master, required my teacher do hard physical labor for 12 years before he taught him the esoteric practices of the inner invisible worlds. And, one day, as my teacher related the story, Sivananda called him into his room and in less than a few hours taught him all the esoteric practices. My teacher's physical vessel had been made strong by hard labor, and in that mode he was able to immediately receive the more subtle teachings, without having to meditate for years.

Today many who seek spiritual wisdom or enlightenment head off to spas, ashrams and retreats without recognizing the importance of strengthening the physical body. Matter and Energy and Information are all related. We live in a world of Matter, so we must start by supporting the physical frame; this opens the door to becoming a Master of the forces within us.

In a research study conducted on mood disorders, including depression, schizophrenia and bipolar disorder, subjects were given physical work on a farm. This kind of labor had a significant and positive effect. Subjects gained self-confidence and increased their ability to cope with everyday stresses. Their counterparts who had stayed with standard care alone showed no such improvements.

The Siddhars focused initially on supporting the physical body because they recognized that the visible world of Matter needed to be in resonance before one could fully explore the invisible worlds. I know many people who pursue meditative practices for years, but their minds are perturbed and they cannot sit still. In these instances, a Siddhar would counsel that the physical body, the Annamaya Kosha, is weak and in dissonance. It would be best for many of these individuals to do a good hard workout first, then sit and meditate. We'll look more closely at these principles in the chapters that follow.

PART 3

Siddha's Model of the Human System

CHAPTER 7

The Temple Within

So far we've looked at the influence of reductionist thinking on both Western healthcare as well as Western adaptations of Eastern traditions. This Part will introduce my perspective as a systems engineer, as well as the authentic teachings of the Siddha health tradition, unadulterated by Western adaptation. As you'll see, this is a comprehensive, systematic view of what it means to be human, a view in which reductionism plays no part.

I mentioned earlier that the ancient Siddhars were practical thinkers. That's also my orientation, and it's the perspective I want to emphasize in the balance of this book. In one word, I'm an engineer. But what does that mean?

>> Engineering is about tangible reality, and how to make progress in the environment of tangible reality.

>> Engineers are workhorses who get things done, while New Age gurus or professors in academia propose and theorise. Engineers have to build things with constraints and imperfections, which are open to ongoing revision and refinement.

>> Engineers value individual elements (reductionism) and overall design (holism), but they engineers are basically connectors who convert theory into an integrated, high-functioning reality.

>> Engineers know that Nature is the greatest engineer of all. Working over billions of years, Nature itself has a goal, and unfolds on itself to create its own designs, and constantly tests new "designs" through mutations.

>> The principles of Nature are Transport, Conversion, and Structure, just as these are the principles of systems theory. More than 5000 years ago the Siddhars of India understood this, using their own unique terminology. Let's now look closely at their understanding.

The Siddhars taught that there is a temple within each of us. But what exactly does that mean? Is this a spiritual concept? And where exactly is this temple located? How do we find it?

The concept of a "temple within" is not based on mysticism. The ancient Siddhars were considered radicals because they opposed many of the mystical religious traditions then prevalent in India. They were focused on the quest for Truth and that state of perfection, known as Siddhi. They were against codified scriptures, superstition, blind devotion, and guru worship. Although they were not atheistic or agnostic, they had no real concept of deities as we think of them now. They considered themselves scientists, not mystics.

In the Siddha tradition, everything is related to science. It all started with unmanifest energy, which the Siddhars called Purusha or consciousness. When consciousness awakens, energy appears and interacts; and then Nature unfolds from energy to matter, through various levels. Siddha is about understanding the body and the physical nature of man. But Siddha concepts concerning the human body and the physical nature of man are quite different from what we learn here in the West.

The Siddhars as scientists developed their precise model of a person based on their experiments and observations. They came to the fundamental conclusion that the human body possessed a complete infrastructure to find truth at all levels of existence.

This thesis is different from the Western view of the human being. Siddhar research led to an important conclusion, one as real as gravity: each one of us is made up of three separate and interconnected systems: The Visible Body; The Invisible Body; and the Atman, the infinite and unknowable. Western medicine is primarily concerned with the physical or visible body. Siddhars said that if we want to understand the puzzle that is man, we need to take all three systems into account. If we fail to do this, we are not seeing the whole picture.

An important point to remember: Siddhars taught that both the visible self and the invisible self were part of the manifest material world. In short, both the seen and the unseen human systems are described as a continuum between matter and energy --- the visible self having more matter and the invisible self being composed of more energy. They acknowledged that some things are not visible to the human eye but that doesn't make them any less real and tangible. Here, again, are the three systems that make up the individual man or woman.

The Visible Self -- Discussions of the Visible Self include all the parts of self that can be heard, felt, smelled, seen or touched.

The Invisible Self -- Discussions of the invisible self include our emotional and spiritual selves; they include our five senses, as well as our various states of mind, including the conscious state, subconscious state, unconscious state, and dream state. Our invisible self also includes our memories, thoughts, wisdom, and common sense, which is called Buddhi (and pronounced boodhi). When I was growing up and my mother wanted to remind me to pay attention to what I was doing, she would tell me, "Use your Buddhi".

The Atman, or soul -- The Siddhas spent very little time discussing the atman or soul and left this in the realm of the unknowable, which could only be experienced by traversing across the visible and invisible worlds within. They focused, instead, on the visible and the invisible self, performing research and study to discover a system to enable each individual to uniquely pursue that journey within, through the right amount of food to support the physical body, and exercises and meditative practices to support the invisible bodies.

CHAPTER 8

The Architecture of Existence

The foundational elements of Siddha are conveyed in a native systems architecture that organizes and describes all existence, from the smallest and most subtle elements to the largest. This system also reveals core principles that provide a model for regulating one's life towards optimal health.

The systems architecture of Siddha is presented in a multi-layered fashion with a particular terminology that describes the elements at each layer. To anyone unfamiliar with Siddha, this terminology may seem obscure or even "mystical." Our immediate focus, therefore, will be to present and explain this terminology layer by layer.

The first layer is known as *Purusha*. Purusha is best described as consciousness, which expresses itself as will, desire, or motivation.

Purusha is said to give rise to *Prakriti*, the second layer, which represents all material existence that is manifested out of Purusha. A goal or an idea, for example, is representative of Purusha. The expression of that idea in some material form is known as Prakriti. In Indian metaphysics, the entire universe was formed from an idea/thought/will/desire (Purusha) that gave rise to the material existence (Prakriti) that we experiences as matter, energy and information.

Prakriti manifests itself in three forms or aspects of energy. These are known as the Gunas: Sattvic, Rajasic, and Tamasic. The Gunas are the "flavors" of Prakriti, each having its own particular subtle qualities. The Gunas are qualities of subtle energy that cannot be seen, touched, tasted, heard or smelled.

In the next layer of architecture, however, the Gunas manifest in material forms that can be engaged by the five senses. When the Gunas materialize in this way, they are known as the Panchabuthas, or the "five elements." Unlike modern physics, the term "elements" does not refer to elements from the periodic table, but is closer to "states of matter."

The five elements in the Siddha and Ayurveda terminologies, along with their English translations, are below:

Siddha	Ayurveda	English
Akayam	Akasha	Space
Vayu	Vayu	Air
Thee	Agni	Fire
Neer	Jala	Water
Mann	Prithvi	Earth

Practitioners of Siddha and Ayurveda use the interaction of these five elements to understand the dynamics of all nature. In the human body, the Panchabuthas mix with each other in various proportions to form physiological entities such as tissues, as well as to define the whole organism. The Panchabuthas are important in Indian medicine because they give rise to individual constitutions and body types.

The notion of body constitution is presented in the fifth layer through the concept of three *doshas*. Our bodies are space, in which air circulates; they have "fire," expressed as heat; and they have solid structure, made of water and earth. Each of these three components is identified with one of the doshas, which are known as *Vata*, *Pitta* and *Kapha*:

Three Doshas	Panchabuthas
Vata	Space + Air
Pitta	Fire
Kapha	Water & Earth

Every human body is composed of combinations of these elements, and this combination is central to Siddha and Ayurveda's conception of health and well-being. The specific combination of doshas is present at birth and determines the body type of the individual. This body type is known as the individual's *Prakriti*.

The sixth layer is composed of seven *Dhatus*. The Vata, Pitta, and Kapha constituents of an individual control the nature of that person's Dhatus, which are closely related to tissues in human physiology. The

Dhatus, in the Siddha and Ayurveda terminologies, along with their English translation, are in the chart below:

Siddha	Ayurveda	English
Enbu	Asthi	Bone
Cheneer	Rakta	Blood
Moolai	Majja	Marrow
Sukila/Sronitha	Shukra	Reproductive Tissues
Saram	Rasa	Plasma
Oon	Mamsa	Muscle
Kozhuppu	Meddha	Fat

The seventh layer is the *Kosha*, which is the whole body of the organism. The body includes the *Indriyas*, which are the fives senses; *Manas*, which represent the mind; and, the *Karmendriyas*, which represent the physical organs.

CHAPTER 9

Layers of the Physical Self

As someone trained in computer science and in applied mechanics, I learned that systems architecture includes three important principles:

>> Layering
>> Transport of energy
>> Intelligent sensing

Each of a system's layers provides a particular function for the overall system. Transport and communication of energy occurs across these layers through channels or networks, which transfer matter, energy and information from outside to the inside. Intelligent sensing of events across layers exists to protect and support the overall system.

Consider the architecture of your home. It too has layers. Your home has an outer layer, which is the exterior of the building, which is visible to everyone.

This outer layer may have a wonderful design, carvings, and/or glass to make it attractive to those who pass by. The middle layer is the foundation and structure of the building; except for the carpenters and construction people, who built it, few may have seen the internal studs, wiring and structure. The inside of the home is the one that you some can see, after they have been allowed in. It is your "home sweet home", with painted walls, pictures, furniture and other decorations.

From outside the building, you bring in piping, electrical and cabling networks, which cuts across the layers to provide water (matter), electricity (energy) and video (information). Most homes have windows, alarm systems or a dog, cameras and other elements to sense what is going on inside and outside, to protect and provide intelligent maintenance of the infrastructure.

This model of your home can be an entrance point to Siddhas model of the human body as a layered entity. Siddha teaches that the human body had five layers known as koshas. The first outer layer was what everyone sees, your visible body. The four inner layers, like the middle layer of your home, provided the location of the "wiring ", and communications infrastructure. The innermost point was the place of the unknown, Purusha, or the infinite. One had to traverse across all the layers to come that innermost point, that "home sweet home".

Energy is brought in from the outside to you on what they called the Sutratma (or "Silver Cord"). The Sutratma when it coalesced with your body, traversed the inner layers of your body through an internal transmission and communication network known as Nadis. These Nadis also had some major communication hubs, seven of them, known as Chakras. An internal system of sensations and movement provides intelligence and motion for one to move in the outer and inner worlds. We'll look more closely at this in the chapters below.

Given the architectural overview using the home as metaphor, we are now ready to explore and better appreciate the unified model of the human building the Siddhars discovered and modeled.

I will always remember the complexity of the temples in Southern India is their complexity. There are multiple rooms, towers, corridors, sanctuaries, and shrines. The temple located within the human body is no less complex. In fact, Siddha teachings describe five separate bodies or selves, which they called Koshas, the inner structural layers of this temple within.

If an ancient Siddhar were to draw an outline of the human body, what would we see? Well, to begin with, we would actually see five separate outlines, one within each other. The outline drawing would resemble an outline of those Russian dolls called babushkas that fit into each other. You can only see the outer doll, but when you begin taking them apart, you find new layers. Some people liken the Siddha view of the body to an onion. We take off the top layer, and then there is another, and then another.

The Siddhas taught that for every human being there are actually five separate bodies, which they called Koshas. The word Kosha translates as sheath or covering. These sheaths start with the first outermost layer. This is the visible one we can see. They then continue through the other four, all part of the invisible body.

As you read about these Koshas, you will notice that the Sanskrit term "maya" is included in each name. Maya translates as "illusion." Even though the Siddhars saw the koshas as being part of the material world, they still included the term "illusion" when describing them relative to the ultimate truth, which is unknowable and indescribable. Similar to other Eastern traditions, Siddhas questioned our tendency to believe that what we see is the only reality. Maya is often likened to a veil that clouds our vision and keeps us from recognizing a deeper truth.

When we talk about entering the temple within, the koshas are like veils that need to be pulled back in order to find the atman, the essence of who we truly are, the infinite Purusha within each of us. Many Westerners are familiar with Namaste, the Sanskrit phrase of greeting and farewell. When we say, "Namaste" to one another, we are really saying "The truth (or true spirit) within me bows down to the truth within you."

1st body or Sheath: The Annamaya Kosha

This is the physical body. Let's look at the word, Annamaya. Anna means food or manifest matter. Maya, as we said, is translated as illusion. Annamaya thus means giving the illusion of food or matter. This first kosha represents all the parts of the flesh and bones person that are dependent on food and oxygen. We can see it, touch it, or find it with current medical technology like x-rays and scans.

2nd body or Sheath: The Pranamaya Kosha

This is the topmost layer, or the membrane of the invisible body, and encases all the other three invisible bodies. This layer is associated with Prana or life force, and hence with life itself. It is an important layer, for it contains the energetic continuum or "electrical network" and bridges the visible body to the more subtle invisible layers. It is also associated with breath. So long as this sheath is there to receive Prana and send it out to all parts of the body, the organism is a living, vital being. This 2nd Kosha is more subtle than the first, but it has definite functions. It contains all the forms of Prana and is connected with physical feelings and bodily functions that we associate with being alive such as hunger, thirst, and elimination.

3rd body or Sheath: The Manomaya Kosha

As we work our way inward, the Manomaya Kosha is called the mind or mental Sheath. However, "mind" in the Siddha System has two parts—lower mind and higher mind. Manomaya is the lower mind. It is connected with the more emotional aspects of the mind and is also associated with the five senses of touch, taste, smell, sound, and sight. This part of mind experiences a wide range of feelings such as pain and pleasure, doubt and fear, longing and passion. It is also associated with mental practices such as memorization. When you do crossword puzzles, play games like Sudoku and Scrabble, or study for exams in just about all subjects, ranging from algebra to zoology, you are using your manomaya Kosha

4th body or Sheath: The Vijnanamaya Kosha

Vijnana translates as knowing, and this Sheath represents higher intelligence. This is associated with a level of wisdom that goes far deeper than the ability to get good grades or become an acknowledged Chess Master. When the Siddhar Rishis talked about somebody showing Vijnana Kosha, they were talking about a person who had left ego aside and was wise enough to seek "Truth" with a capital T.

The Vijnana Kosha reminds us to differentiate between the qualities of being smart and clever as found in the 3rd Sheath and being really intelligent and wise as illustrated by the 4th Sheath. There is an amusing tale that I first heard from one of my teachers, which illustrates some of the differences between lower mind and higher mind.

This story begins with a village in ancient India that is being harassed by a snake—a large cobra, who bites and has all the villagers so terrified that they are afraid to leave their homes. Finally a Siddha Rishi comes into town, and the villagers tell him their problem. "I'll go talk to the snake," he says.

"No," the villagers tell him. "You can't do that!"

But the Rishi has no fear, so he goes out in the environs around the village and meets up with the snake. The Rishi has a heart-to-heart with the snake and convinces him that there is more to life than biting and

230

scaring people. The snake is amazingly receptive, and the Rishi teaches him to meditate.

The following day the snake goes out and starts meditating on a rock in the sun. Some villagers, who come by and notice that the snake has lost his frightening persona, start throwing rocks and sticks at it. Bloody and bruised, the snake runs off to hide in a hole. The following day, the same thing happens. The snake is trying to be a peaceful snake, but he is getting hurt in the process and becoming quite discouraged. The next day the Siddhar is out walking and the snake who sees him, hurries up to him and says,

"Listen, I'm here meditating trying to be a good snake and do the right thing, but people don't understand that I've changed. They are really hurting me, and I don't know what to do."

"The Siddhar tells him, "I did teach you to meditate. I did tell you not to bite people. But I didn't tell you to stop hissing at people when they come near you with sticks and stone. You have to have some intelligence and wisdom about life.

Peeling back the Vijnanamaya Kosha—the 4th Sheath and seeing its true meaning means that we will be able to leave fantasy and illusion behind and observe reality-- what we are actually doing and what is really happening in the world around us.

The 5th Body or Sheath: The Anandamaya Kosha

Ananda is translated as bliss, and this Kosha is known as the Sheath of Bliss. Within man, this the innermost Kosha closest to the soul within each of us, is

231

seen as a reflection of Atman. We are most likely to experience this Kosha when we are in the very deepest sleep or deep meditation.

Experiencing this fifth Kosha, as Buddha said, is one of the most dangerous experiences. How can bliss be dangerous? The bliss at this stage can be so wonderful, that one can become attached to this Kosha and never want to leave.

The Siddhars said that all Koshas were maya, illusion, for they were still part of the material realms, be it visible or invisible. Even this most subtle Kosha is maya, for attachment to this state of bliss may prevent one moving onward to Purusha, the Infinite within us.

The sheaths from the first through the fifth traverse a continuum of matter and energy. The first sheath is clearly made up of largely matter; whereas, the fifth sheath is made up of pure energy, leading to the Infinite, known as Purusha, which is pure Information.

CHAPTER 10

Prana, the Energy That Keeps Us Alive

When we speak of the invisible or inner self, we all know what we mean. We know intuitively that the ungraspable invisible self is all about energy. In Siddha, the invisible self is formed from Sattvic and Rajasic energy, and is associated with the basic life force or energy known as Prana.

Prana is the energy that moves across the various Khosas, no different than the electricity and water that moves through your home, in between all the layers. Having Prana means that we are alive. Anyone who has ever witnessed a live birth, or even seen one on television, can attest to the excitement surrounding the moment itself. The almost lifeless looking infant emerges. Suddenly there is a cry. The infant is alive and breathing on its own, apart from its mother. A new life has entered the world. Watchers typically experience an impulse to cheer.

We can perceive our bodies in many ways, but most of us know that we are more complicated than the flesh, blood, bones, and tissue that make up our material bodies. What is that intangible force that enters the body at birth and shows itself with a baby's first cry? Siddhars, like other Eastern cultures, used the word Prana to describe the vital energy that means that we are alive.

Prana carries with it matter, energy and information. The Siddha system allows for different kinds of Prana or energy. The first, which is responsible for breath, heartbeat, and nerve impulses, is the vital current that shows that we are alive. With each breath we take, Prana enters our body and makes its way into the circulatory system and to each cell of the body. Other forms of Prana are connected to temperature, digestion, sound, conscious energy, voluntary muscular system, excretion and the body's elimination processes.

In Asia particularly, advanced practitioners of esoteric yoga techniques spend years training themselves to control and manipulate "Prana" in their bodies. This practice is known as Pranayama. There are many credible examples of yogis who have been able to control breath, body temperature, and other physical actions in ways that are almost impossible to understand and seem almost miraculous (or fraudulent) when viewed by observers who are unfamiliar with these practices.

If Prana carries information, and access to information requires consciousness, where does consciousness come from? And how do we get it? Because we are all intrinsically connected to the larger universe, it makes sense that we would be getting our consciousness as well as our essential life force from a source connected to nature.

Siddha teachings say that at the moment of birth, consciousness and energy enter our body through the umbilical cord as we take our first independent breath. The teachings about this are very specific. They describe 64 streams of energy that enter the body in this way. These energy streams, which are called the sutratma, carry Prana as consciousness with the information to connect us to the universe.

Thirty energy streams of the sutratma travel down; thirty travel up; two travel across in one direction; and two more go across in the other direction. In this way, the sutratma branch out throughout the body and create a network of 72,000 channels of energy, known as Nadi lines that connect various parts of the body.

The Sutratma are an important element in the Siddhar spiritual belief system. They are the essential way we, as microcosms, stay connected to the macrocosm that is the universe. As long as we are alive, we continue to receive energy through these streams. Siddhar teachings also say that an energy knot or cord, formed by the Sutratma, at the umbilicus is connected to the inner self and keeps it from floating away from our visible body. At the time of death, that connection is broken, and the inner self is free to separate and prepare for a new incarnation.

The concept of a cord or thread keeping one's inner self connected to the physical body is common to other belief systems. Anyone who has ever read or heard about astral projection or travel may remember practitioners talking about a "silver cord" connecting the astral and physical body.

Here in the West, those who are interested in more metaphysical studies sometimes quote a "silver cord" reference found in the Old Testament Book of Ecclesiastes: "For man goes to his everlasting home, and the mourners go about the streets. Remember him before *the silver cord* is snapped and the golden bowl is broken, before the pitcher is shattered at the spring and the wheel broken at the well, before the dust returns to the earth as it began, and the spirit returns to God who gave it."

The Sutratma that bring us consciousness and connect us to the universe have another important function. They also represent the connection that exists between us, as individual beings. As parts of the whole, we are all interconnected.

After the Sutratma enter our visible and invisible bodies, they branch out and form Nadi Lines. These are the channels that carry Prana that moves and flows throughout the Koshas. They carry all forms of energy, including mental, emotional, and psychic—even consciousness in the form of energy.

The Nadis are like cabling or fiber optic lines providing power for the whole structure that is the human body. The ancients of Siddha viewed the body fundamentally as a matrix of energy. They drew clear pictures of this energy matrix that traverses the entire body like a complex network of rivers and streams.

The Sanskrit word Nadi means river. 72,000 of these nadi lines or rivers of energy penetrate every organ, tissue and call in the body, carrying the life force necessary to keep us functioning.

Ask yourself how you feel today. If you are not quite up to par, it may be because your Nadi lines are blocked and your energy is not able to flow. Siddha practitioners believe that your state of health is directly connected to the Nadi lines in your body. If your Nadi lines are blocked, your health is challenged because the organs and systems of your body are not able to communicate and work together.

Disease is identified as blockages in the nadi streams of energy. Removing these blockages enables the body to be brought into balance, ensuring that all the organs and systems of the body are prepared for optimal performance. Siddha practitioners use a variety of different modalities to "clear" blockages and cleanse the Nadi lines. These include herbs, massage, yoga, diet, meditation, music, and light.

While it is said that each of us has 72,000 Nadi lines crisscrossing the body, there are three major Nadi lines, and they are of enormous importance in the Siddha system.

Line One is called Sushumna
Line Two is called Ida
Line Three is called Pingala

It is much less important to remember these names than to remember what they do.

Sushumna, the largest and most important Nadi runs along the center of the spinal column. It is a river of energy that extends from the 1st chakra at the base of the spine and goes straight up all the way up to the crown chakra. When the channel of energy known as Sushumna is unblocked, energy is able to freely flow up and down through the body and up to the brain.

Transporting Prana from the left nostril, the Ida line twists around the spine in helical fashion. This Nadi or energy channel runs between the 1st or base chakra and the 6th Chakra, which relates to the third eye. Ida is associated with the moon and with a more passive and receptive energy. It is said to be "cooling" in temperature and connected to right brain activities such as intuition, feeling, visual skills, and creativity.

Pingala, which is Ida's counterpart, transports Prana from the right nostril. Like the Ida it twists around the spine, connecting the lower chakras and the 6th. Pingala, which is associated with the hot sun and a more extroverted and active energy, is connected to left brain skills such as logic, organization, and mathematics.

It makes sense that at certain places in the body, these nadi lines will come together and form important intersections. The ancients identified 107 of these intersections, which were seen as energy points or "marma" points. These energy points became the basis of acupuncture points, which were developed by traveling Chinese monks who came to visit the Buddha in India. Seven of these marma points are seen as powerful super-intersections. These are the chakras.

CHAPTER 11

The Chakras: Siddha Anatomy of Energy

We discussed chakras earlier as the basis of modern Eastern reductionism. Here, let's look at the original meaning of the chakra anatomical system as the energy centers of our invisible bodies. They cannot be seen on x-rays, or MRIs or CAT scans. The Chakra System was originally developed as a Hindu concept in India, but Chakras have a role in Buddhism as well.

The word "chakra" means wheel. In works of art, chakras are often depicted as almost flower like spinning centers of energy with a number of petals. The petals represent the number of nadis carrying energy to and from the individual chakra. In the Siddha System, we each have seven chakras.

The Chakras located in the lower part of the body are seen as being more instinctual; those on the upper part are described as being more mental. All of these Chakras receive and send out energy through the Nadi channels.

1) The Root Chakra

This chakra is located at the base of the spine. If you were to sit down cross-legged, the root chakra is there where your bottom hits the earth, between the base of the genitals and the anus. Much of your life force and Prana is stored in the chakra, which keeps your grounded and connected to life itself. The ancients taught that meditating on this chakra gave yoga practitioners awareness of the power of kundalini. When your root chakra is open and appropriately active, you feel yourself as being grounded and at home in your world. When the Root Chakra is inactive and closed, you tend to be uncomfortable in your environment; you may resist change and become more materialist. This chakra is often depicted as having four petals or Nadis branching out.

2) The Sacral Chakra

This Chakra is located in the main Nadi energy channel known as Sushumna at the base of the genitals. It is associated with sexuality and procreation, as well as elimination. When the Sacral Chakra is appropriately open, you are able to express your emotions and have an easier time with intimacy. When it is over-active, you are likely to be over-emotional and your libido may be too highly charged and all over the place. If the Sacral Chakra is closed and under-active, you probably keep your emotions too tightly under-wrap. This chakra is seen as having six Nadis which radiate from its center.

3) The Solar Plexus Chakra

This Chakra is found in the Sushumna Energy channel right near the navel. Associated with the solar plexus and the element of fire, it controls the liver and stomach. The Solar Plexus Chakra is associated with self-esteem and confidence. When it is appropriately open, you have balanced sense of self-esteem. If it is over-active, you might be accused of being "too full of yourself." If it is underactive or closed, you will tend to feel indecisive and unsure of yourself. The Solar Plexus Chakra has ten radiating Nadis.

4) The Heart Chakra

This Chakra is located in the Sushumna Nadi energy channel in the region of the heart and is associated with all heart function and with the element of air. Located near the heart, it is associated with our ability to feel love and compassion in its highest form. If it is over-active, the people around you may tend to feel "suffocated" by your love. If it is under-active, your nearest and dearest might accuse you of "holding back" and being unable to open up to love. The Heart Chakra is shown with fifteen nadis.

5) The Throat Chakra

This Chakra, located within the Sushumna Nadi at the base of the throat, is associated with the element of ether. This chakra is related to all forms of self-expression including speech and art. If your throat chakra is appropriately open, you have no difficulty expressing yourself. If it is over-active, people around

241

you may feel that you are overly dominating; they may say that you "never listen," and wear them down with your opinions. If it is under-active, you have a difficult time "finding your voice." This chakra is depicted with sixteen Nadis.

6) The Third Eye Chakra

Located within the Sushumna Nadi, between the eyebrows, this chakra is sometimes called the Brow Chakra and referred to as the seat of consciousness. It is often associated with the pineal gland. When it is appropriately open, you are able to be intuitive and perceptive without losing sight of reality. When it is closed, even friends might say that you lack perception and are unable to be open-minded. If it is over-active, you will have a tendency to live in a fantasy world. The third eye is often used as a symbol of enlightenment. Yogis train the third-eye in order to make their visions manifest in the real world; it is also used to help expand consciousness. This chakra has two nadis, which radiate from its center.

7) The Crown Chakra

Located just above the crown of the head, the Crown Chakra is associated with activities of the brain. It is often described as radiating light and is associated with wisdom and cosmic consciousness. When this chakra is appropriately open and balanced, you are aware of what is going on around you in the world and are able to incorporate spirituality into your life. If it is over-active, you may have a tendency to live in your head and be too cerebral. If it is under-active, you may close yourself off to spiritual or more evolved aspects of yourself. The Crown Chakra is said to have a thousand Nadis radiating out from it.

PART FOUR

Systems Theory and Practice

CHAPTER 12

A Toolbox of Practical Concepts

Having gained an overview of the human body as understood by Siddha, in Part Nine we'll look at the same elements in light of the newest innovations in Western science -- especially systems theory, a highly practical, results-oriented approach to even the most complex issues of life in the modern world.

We'll begin with a concise but comprehensive explanation of the principles of systems theory. This will be very different from the kind of dry exposition you might expect in an academic journal or university lecture hall. You'll quickly see how revolutionary a systems approach can be, and in subsequent chapters you'll be able to use this approach to illuminate ancient wisdom, modern science, and how to optimize the day to day experience of living inside your own human body.

Systems theory is a toolbox of practical concepts, similar to the scientific understanding of gravity or electromagnetism. It's a very organized and logical way of comprehending the forces that operate in the world. Using systems theory, things that previously seemed random or mysterious can be understood completely and intelligently.

A system is a set of objects or energies working together for a specific goal or purpose. The first step toward understanding systems theory is recognizing the connections between elements that might once have seemed separate but are actually linked together in a system.

Systems can be simple or infinitely complex. A wristwatch, a cow, a human heart, a city, and a washing machine are all systems – as is the Earth itself and even the whole universe. Your body is a system with many subsystems within it. Once you understand how systems work, you can understand how anything works.

To achieve any goal, you will need to understand how intelligent systems function. But before we go there, we will begin by understanding how open systems work. A toaster and an electric heater are examples of open systems. But the presence of a self-correcting thermostat makes your home heating system an intelligent system.

All systems include five basic elements: Input, Output, Transport, Conversion, and Structure.

Input is the stuff coming into a system. There can be a single input or multiple inputs. An input can be information, matter, or energy. For example, what did you have to eat today? Did you get any exercise, or did you stay in bed all afternoon? What did you see out the window? What music did you listen to? Whom did you speak with on the phone?

Output is the stuff coming out of a system. This can be a single output or multiple outputs and, like input, output can be information, matter, or energy. The output is the direct result of the inputs (the karma) into a system. If you somehow plugged your toaster into a nuclear power plant, there would be too much electrical input. This would cause a negative output: your toaster blows up. But if you try to light a city with flashlight batteries, you'll get a negative output for the opposite reason: too little input. Depending on the situation, not enough can be as bad as too much.

Transport is the principle of movement in a system: the process of information, matter, or energy moving from input to output, from karma to karma-phal, from cause to effect. It's the presence or absence of dynamic progress of stuff moving from source to destination. In a computer, transport is the aspect of the machine's process of moving information, bits of ones and zeroes, through the system, from the keyboard (input) to the screen display (output). When purchasing a computer, you may want one that does this very quickly, or you may need to focus on something else.

Conversion in systems theory refers to the process of transforming or converting an Input into an Output. The force of conversion changes information, matter, or energy from one form to another. The Central

248

Processing Unit (CPU) of a computer, along with the necessary software, embodies conversion. When you input three symbols on the keyboard ("1 + 1", for example) the CPU converts those symbols into an output, which is "2."

Structure refers to the boundaries, connections, and overall internal environment <u>within</u> which the activities of transport and conversion take place. Structure is sometimes referred to as the storage aspect of a system. A car, whether it's a racer or a SUV, needs a body or frame made of metal, rubber, and plastic. Both a fighter jet and a passenger plane need the fuselage, which holds the cockpit, seats, and engines. Health, physical strength, and emotional stability are structural aspects of a human system.

CHAPTER 13

Open Systems and Intelligent Systems

An open system provides a particular Output from a particular Input. Once the Input is set, the Output is set. A basic electric room heater is another everyday example of an open system. Assuming the heater is plugged into the wall, turning the heater ON and setting it to a particular level – the Inputs of LOW, MEDIUM or HIGH -- results in a certain amount of heat, which is the Output. Transport is the process of transporting electric current from the wall socket into the heater, as well as the heat from the heating coils into the room. Conversion, represented by the heating coils, is what transforms the electrical energy into heat or thermal energy. The Structure element is the entire unit that contains all the components of the system.

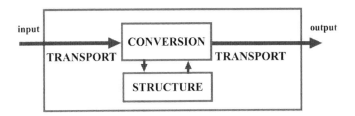

All open systems take in an Input and produce a specific Output. One underlying assumption of open systems is that the Output maintains itself as long as the Input is maintained. Human beings can also be open systems — and there's nothing wrong with that, if it's a conscious choice. The assumption is, for example, you show up to work, work hard and you get as Output a steady income, a stable relationship, and security --- all of which are worthwhile desires. They are certainly what most people hoped for and wanted during much of American history.

But now life is more fluid, unstable and improvisational. Change happens faster. It's no longer easy to even imagine what things were like before laptops and cellphones, even though they've only been around for a relatively short time.

So let's be clear about the relationship between the Input and Output in open systems. An open system provides for a stable and predictable result that is as close to being guaranteed as it can possibly be. If external disturbances occur that affect the result --- the Output --- open systems are not capable of self-correction or self-regulation to adjust the system in order to obtain the original Output. And once again, there's

251

nothing wrong with getting predictable results from well-understood and conventional actions, provided it's what you really want. But that's becoming more difficult in a world where rapid change is the norm. New technologies and historical changes are demanding that we be more flexible and resilient. For survival and success in that world, an open system existence might no longer be the best choice.

Intelligent systems include four additional elements: a Goal; Disturbances; a Sensor; and, a Controller. These elements enable self-regulation and continuous adjustment of the Input in order to achieve a desired Output that matches the Goal. Using a Sensor and a Controller, this can be achieved in spite of Disturbances to the system.

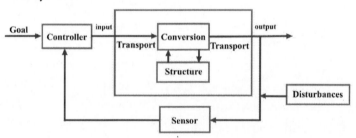

Unlike an open system, an intelligent system begins with a Goal, an intention, (or a Dharma or Sankalpa as they are referred to in Siddha). Setting this Goal is your responsibility and the Goal must be chosen wisely. The entire process of being "intelligent" exists to achieve that Goal, in spite of any Disturbances that occur.

Disturbances are those things that get in the way of achieving our Goal. They can be physical obstacles, or procrastination, inability to focus, and poor eating habits.

In Siddha, obstacles were known as vikaras. The ancient Siddhars meticulously itemized all the known vikaras a human may face in a lifetime.

But here is the secret: if we can use and refine our Sensors to know the current Output --- where we are at right now, and then use and develop our Controller to measure the difference between where we want to go --- our Goal and our Output to strategically figure out a new Input to affect the forces of Transport, Conversion and Storage to get a desired Output, we can move closer to our Goal. And, this process occurs over time as we go around the loop, and each time getting closer to our Goal. We do this by "closing the loop" of the open system, by feeding back the Output of the open system to a Sensor, which is used to measure the actual Output.

In the Siddha tradition, the Sensor was known as the Indriyas of the human body --- the Indriyas were our literal senses of smell, touch, sight, taste and hearing. How well the Sensor can measure is critical to knowing exactly where we are. A poor Sensor can give us an erroneous measure of the Output, and this will affect the decisions of the Controller. In Siddha, the purpose of awareness practices such as meditation, yoga and other spiritual activities was to enhance one's indriyas (sensors). The more our sensors are refined, the closer one can get to the Goal or Sankalpa.

The Controller (or Manas in Siddha) literally measures the difference between our Goal and the actual Output to make a decision on what new Input (or Karma) we need to send back into the system to affect changes in the forces of Transport (Vata), Conversion

253

(Pitta) and Storage (Kapha), to get a new Output (Karma-Phal).

The Controller element is perhaps the most important aspect of intelligent systems. The Controller is all about making decisions. By integrating the Goal with information coming in from the Sensors, the Controller makes decisions which result in actions that are new Inputs into the system. These Inputs result in the Transport and Conversion of information, matter, and energy within a Structure, which leads to a new Output. As the sequence takes place and we become aware of the Output from our actions, the Controller draws on this awareness to make a subsequent decision. This results in a new Input. Based on that new Input, the process of Transport and Conversion of information, matter, and energy within a Structure is reiterated and refined.

When Disturbances are encountered, the system must course-correct back toward the Goal. Because this is a continuous process, it's critical that awareness and information – and the decisions that result – can be made on the fly. The more refined our awareness becomes by developing our Sensors, the better our decisions will be. For this reason, spiritual practices, which promote stillness and refinement of our awareness --- the Sensors, enable a clearer perception of what is really taking place and to see the Output with accuracy as it really is. This in turn allows the Controller to make better decisions. When in doubt, therefore, it's important to be still and refine your awareness.

Rather than a strictly spiritual approach, this is a principle of modern systems theory. It is also the essence of Siddha, which teaches stillness as a path to awareness, right decisions, and right action – which together result in the Output of achieving the Goal we desire. In both systems theory and Siddha, this process is what intelligence really means. At any point in life, we can simply be reactive to what's happening around us, or we can set and approach our goals based on awareness, intention, and intelligence.

Every journey begins with a Goal and some level of awareness. As our awareness becomes more refined, our Controller can make decisions that translate the forces of information, matter, and energy into transport and conversion within a structure that leads toward the goal. The key lies in continuing the process of refining awareness and information, which may even lead to refining or redefining the Goal itself.

CHAPTER 14

Intelligent Systems In Your Home

To make the concept of intelligent systems more real and practical, let's consider a home's central heating system that includes a thermostat. It's a good example of how an intelligent system works. Unlike the open system heater we discussed earlier, this "intelligent" system provides for constant refinement and adjustment of the Input to achieve an Output that matches a specific Goal. Let's first identify the nine components of the intelligent system using the home heating system.

Goal: If the desired temperature for the apartment is 78 degrees, that's the Goal. It is achieved when the apartment's actual temperature (the Output) and the selected Goal are equal.

Disturbances: The opposite of a Goal, or the opposition to it, are Disturbances. In the thermostat example, the disturbances could be a cold draft from an open window in another room. Resolving Disturbances is the key to achieving the Goal. And, this requires accurate and refined Sensors as well as an effective Controller.

Sensor: The sensor is something that can measure the actual temperature in the room— a thermometer – within the thermostat. The Sensor communicates the actual real room temperature (the Output) to the Controller. One thing to be aware of is that the sensitivity of the Sensor --- how refined it is in measuring the actual room temperature -- will be critical in achieving the goal of 75 degrees.

Controller: The Controller is the component of the thermostat that receives two pieces of information: 1) what the Goal is --- in this case 75 degrees, and 2) the actual room temperature from thermometer, which is the sensor. The Controller takes these two pieces of information and determines the difference between the Goal temperature and the current temperature.

Transport: The forces of Transport in this case are the flow of heating oil into the furnace. If our current temperature --- the Output --- is too low, say only 60 degrees, then the Input will be <u>to increase the transport (or flow)</u> of heating oil into the furnace. More heating oil, more heat. If this happens and the heat goes too high -- say to 80 degrees -- the Controller will send an Input to shut off the flow of heating oil into the furnace.

Conversion: The furnace takes in the heating oil (matter) and converts it into heat (thermal energy). The more oil, the more heat is produced. Less oil, less heat is produced. No oil, then no heat is produced. It's that simple.

Structure: The Structure is composed of the walls, the floors, the insulation, the beams, and the ceiling. These elements form the structure of the house, which provides a container where the forces of Transport and Conversion come together. Clearly, if you have very well insulated home, then the place will need much less oil to heat, and we can achieve and, more importantly, maintain the Goal --- with far less fluctuations. If the home has lots of drafts and poor insulation, heat will escape and the Controller will constantly have to turn on and turn off the flow of oil into the furnace.

Output: The Output is the actual temperature of the room at any point.

The key feature of intelligent systems is that they are always in flux. They are constantly making adjustments. They are sensing, controlling and modulating the input into the open system. "Perfection" is not the objective, but is only an imaginary concept, which is always being approached but is never permanently sustained.

The best way to understand systems theory is always to look at systems in action. Another good everyday example could be making a bowl of soup. But there are two ways of looking at that example. First, we can imagine making soup as an open system process.

It's very simple. Open a can of soup, put the soup in a pan, and turn on the stove for five minutes.

There are three Inputs: (1) opening the can of soup, (2) putting the soup in the bowl, and (3) turning on the stove for five minutes. The heat activates energies of Conversion to cook the soup. The pan provides the Structure. The Transport is the flow of heat energy through the pan and into the soup. After five minutes the Output is heated soup, which is ready to be consumed.

But suppose you were a more ambitious chef who wanted to make a large amount of soup using an intelligent system. What are the elements relative to the intelligent system of making soup?

Let's start with the Goal. We don't want just any bowl of soup. We want a tasty, warm bowl of soup. This is our Goal. So far, so good.

But with any Goal, Disturbances will arise. There might be a power outage or an overflow of water. The kitchen might run out of a key ingredient. An important employee might suddenly quit in a huff. If something can go wrong, it often will. These are the potential Disturbances.

Remember, we achieve our Goal by overcoming Disturbances through the use of our Sensors and a Controller.

In this case, our five senses are the Sensors. We can observe how the soup is coming along by watching it. We can use our ears to hear if it boiling too much? Does something smell like its burning? We can taste it so see if it has enough salt, or if it's too spicy or needs more sour taste. We can stir it and feel it with our hands to see if it's too thick or coarse. Our senses are fed back to our Controller.

The Controller is you, which includes your experience, your intelligence, and your skill as a chef. Are you getting closer to that tasty, warm bowl of soup? Based on this, you decide what action and inputs you are going to take and keep adjusting the inputs, until you achieve our Goal.

The Inputs could include adding or removal of ingredients, choosing to cover the pan, adding more salt, and increasing the flame.

Transport is the movement of heat and mechanical forces inside the pan, including the simple motion of moving heat as we stir the ingredients.

Next comes the energy of Conversion. The fire that heats the soup embodies this energy.

Structure is provided by the cauldron in which the ingredients are cooked and stirred.

The Goal is reached when, after continuously sensing the soup (tasting it, smelling it, touching it) and making adjustments with our Goal in mind, we get an Output, the tasty bowls of homemade soup.

CHAPTER 15

Your Natural Systems State

Intelligent systems are based on the desire to achieve a Goal. According to the wisdom tradition of Siddha, the body has a natural intelligence and it inherently knows its goal --- which is known as its *Prakriti* or its *Natural Systems State*. The Natural System State is the unique combination of the forces of Transport, Conversion and Structure inherent to you as an individual. In Siddha, health is defined as you achieving the goal of your body's Natural System State. Most of us are not even aware of your body's Natural System State. Disturbances, moreover, get in the way and perturb us away from our Natural System State.

But what is your natural systems state? In terms of systems theory, who is it that you really are? The forces of Transport, Conversion, and Structure affect all forms of matter, energy and information throughout nature. The strength of these forces varies from one life form to another. That strength also varies among individuals – including you -- within a given species.

The importance of these variations is being recognized by Western medicine as better diagnostic tools become available and as genome research reveals the individual character of human DNA. But the concept that every person's physiology is a system with an individualized balance of energies has existed for thousands of years. This became clear to me when I received a Fulbright grant that allowed me to return to India for study of the ancient health tradition known as Siddha.

The Siddhars used their own bodies as experimental laboratories to understand the interaction of three essential forces which they called Vata, Pitta, and Kapha.

As we've seen, it's surprising – or maybe it's not surprising – that the Siddha principles of Vata, Pitta, and Kapha are exact parallels of Transport, Conversion, and Structure. Perhaps systems theory is simply a new terminology for an ancient wisdom tradition. Whether we see ourselves as combinations of Transport, Conversion, and Structure -- or of Vata, Pitta, and Kapha -- each of us is a shifting and individualized balance of these energies. It's a balance that needs to be continuously acknowledged, understood, and cared for.

As the forces of nature interact within each of us, some of us have more Transport, others are strongest in Conversion, and still others are dominated by Structure. There are even a few very individuals who have an almost equal presence of each. The varying proportion

262

of these forces is one of the most essential ways in which we are different from each other.

Initially, you need to identify your own Natural System State. Once this has been done, the goal of supporting that state becomes possible. So what is your essential nature? Which forces give direction to your being?

Are you dominated by the force of Transport? Transport expresses itself as sensitivity to variations in flow, mobility, and movement. If Transport is your dominant force and that force is too high, you may feel nervous and agitated. If it's too low, you could feel very lethargic or depressed. Transport is in charge of everything that moves and is kinetic in our bodies, including the flow of energy and information. Because of this, Transport is regarded as the primary force without which Conversion or Structure could not function.

When Transport is not functioning correctly, all the other forces can go awry.

- Are you extremely uncomfortable in cold weather?
- Do you often juggle several activities at once?
- Do you think and talk quickly?
- Do you prefer spontaneity over scheduling?
- Do you tend toward dry skin and hair?
- Are you naturally thin, and do you lose weight easily?
- Do you grasp new ideas quickly, but wish you could remember more of what you learn?

- Do you impulsively start working on projects without thinking them through?
- Do you sometimes skip meals or forget to eat?
- Are you basically optimistic and enthusiastic?

Are you dominated by the force of Conversion?
Conversion manifests as sensitivity to variations in physiological processes such as metabolism and digestion, as well as analytical thinking and decision-making. If the forces of Conversion are not functioning well, you can experience health and emotional problems associated with the inability to convert and transform elements of Matter, Energy and Information.

- Do you very strongly dislike hot weather?
- Are you detail oriented and exceptionally good at processing information and data?
- Do you think things through before taking action?
- Do you metabolize food quickly and efficiently?
- Do view competition as an enjoyable challenge?
- Does your weight fluctuate?
- Do you prefer to have meals on a set schedule?
- Do you become impatient with yourself or others?
- Do you enjoy turning ideas into applications?
- Are your eyes especially sensitive to sunlight?

Are you dominated by the force of Structure?
Structure is the principle of containment for matter, information, and energy. Men and women who are Structure dominant are naturally able to sustain and

tolerate more than other people. Structure forces foster relaxation and calm, and an aura of security. But when Structure is out of balance it can manifest as stubbornness or isolation.

- Do you have a broad body frame?
- Do you tend to be overweight?
- Do you prefer not to move around or travel?
- Are you often called upon to help others?
- Are you not bothered by either hot or cold weather?
- Do you have exceptionally good physical stamina?
- Is your preferred learning style slow and steady?
- Do you easily retain what you've learned?
- Do you take your time moving between activities?
- Do you often have sinus infections or colds?
- Do you try to speak precisely and emphatically?

CHAPTER 16

Identifying Disturbances

Disturbances are part of any journey, including the journey of our lives. Once you become aware of your Natural System State, it's your responsibility to keep that state in balance, despite any turbulence you encounter.

But at any given moment you are likely not operating at the peak of your Natural System State. So how are you right now? How are you feeling today? Is everything going well in your life? Do you feel upbeat and cheerful or do you feel down in the dumps? Are you feeling healthy? Or are you catching a cold?

As a unique and dynamic person, you are not going to be feeling the same every day. Here are some questions to help you get a handle on what the forces of Transport, Conversion, and Structure are doing in your system right now, today. Your answers will help you determine which forces are "off-course." You can then decide how you want to bring that force back into alignment.

Are your Transport forces undergoing disturbances?

- Have you been feeling anxious or overly excited?
- Is your energy level noticeably uneven?
- Are you feeling depressed, or do you have bursts of energy so intense that you have a hard time calming down?
- Do you have any dry spots, chapped, or cracked skin?
- Is your lower GI tract upset? Are you having bouts of diarrhea or constipation? Do you experience gas or bloating?
- Are you forgetting to eat, or are you losing weight?
- Is cold weather bothering you more than usual?
- Are you having difficulty concentrating or finishing projects?
- Are you having joint or arthritic pain?
- Have you been making any impulsive decisions?
- Do you have trouble falling asleep or staying asleep?

Are your Conversion forces undergoing disturbances?

- Are you putting pressure on yourself or others?
- Are you having upper GI problems?
- Are you suffering from heartburn or a sore throat that your doctor thinks is caused by acid reflux?
- Is an aversion to heat becoming more intense?
- Do you need stronger sunglasses than previously?
- Are you easily angered or often impatient?

267

- Have you become noticeably critical of others?
- Do you drink large amounts of water or other beverages?
- Do you have more rashes or cold sores than usual?
- Do you have feelings of jealousy or need to get even?

Are your Structure forces undergoing disturbances?

- Are you having sinusitis, allergies, or congestion?
- Are you able to keep your weight under control?
- Do you crave carbs, chocolate, or other sweets?
- Do you want to sleep all the time?
- Do you have a white coat on your tongue?
- Are you generally feeling lethargic and dull?
- Do you often procrastinate?
- Do you accumulate things you don't need?
- Are you finding it difficult make changes in your life?
- Do you respond to stress with hostility?

By learning which forces are disturbed, you can be the Controller, making adjustments to Inputs that will bring you back to your Natural System State. But the first step is to correctly assess what's wrong. What is the true nature of the disturbance? Be real. Don't look for an easy answer, neither in reductionist science nor in reassuring New Age mysticism.

CHAPTER 17

Controlling the Forces

Assuming you're bringing the right energies into your system, the next step is optimizing the forces of Transport, Conversion, and Structure that process and sustain those energies.

Controlling the Forces of Transport. Transport is expressed through movement. When it's in balance, Transport presents itself as joy, grace, agility and enthusiasm. Both systems theory and Siddha identify three Inputs as essential for Transport to function at an optimal level: warmth, rhythm and lubrication.

Stay Warm

Our bodies, particularly our muscles, work far more efficiently when they are warmed up before any kind of activity or exercise. Muscles contract and relax faster when they are warm. Warmth gives your muscles greater agility, speed, and strength. Warming up is like an insurance policy, decreasing the possibility of injury while also allowing you a greater degree of motion. If you are warm, your blood vessels are dilated, and this reduces stress on your heart and increases the flow (movement) of blood throughout your body. Blood is the key transporter of nutrients in your body. When you stay warm, your blood is able to be more efficient and deliver more oxygenated blood, making your entire system more effective to support motion at multiple levels. It also enables oxygen in your blood to be transported at a greater speed.

Your joints are key to movement and motion. Staying warm enables you to have a wide range of motion. Stiffness, for example, is a symptom that Transport is not working right. Warmth increases production of synovial fluids in your joints, serving to reduce friction, to support that range of motion. Greater range of motion gives you the greater confidence to try new things in a safe manner. Staying warm helps your body secrete the hormones that enable energy production, which is key to Transport. Exhaustion is another symptom telling us that the forces of Transport are not functioning right.

Movement can be erratic and chaotic, methodical and elegant, or graceful and intelligent. Staying warm enables nerve impulses to be transported at greater speeds, resulting in greater focus. This focus in turn will support the right level of concentration in a relaxed manner to provide support for graceful motion.

In order to thrive, Transport needs the Input of warmth. Think about your car on the coldest winter morning. Most of us will go out and warm it up before driving off. The warmth we are talking about is inner warmth, inside of the engine, inside of the car, inside of you. Warm friends, a warm home, and a warm disposition all fuel your inner forces of Transport. By doing those things that build such inner warmth, you directly support the optimal functioning of Transport.

Stay in Rhythm

A sense of rhythm is the ability to move your body to a regular beat. Rhythm or regularity is key to optimal motion and Transport. A person who dances well moves to a regular rhythm. A great drummer follows a great beat. Musicians often train with a metronome, an instrument that puts out a constant beat, to help them keep their rhythm. One of my mentors Frank Zane, the great body builder, taught me to lift weights to a metronome, or to a beat. When one does this, it makes it much easier, and more fluid. One can move and Transport with greater ease.

Because the force of Transport drives so many important body processes, it requires this level of regularity. Breathing, digestion and elimination are all dependent on proper rhythm and regularity. Having a regular schedule, eating at regular times, and sleeping and waking regularly is all about being in rhythm, which makes Transport far more effective. As someone said, "repetition is the mother of skill."

Siddha masters recommended that their students follow a schedule--early to bed, early to rise, routinized mealtimes, and play and work at particular hours. They were very demanding about the need for such regularity. In fact, in all spiritual practices, regularity is more important than the length of practice. Some people will meditate for 2 hours for a few weeks, and then stop, without any semblance of discipline. It is better to do less, but with consistency to achieve the best results. The highest level of rhythm and regularity is critical for the force of Transport.

In our breathing, the forces of Transport manifest themselves most clearly. Without breath our entire being ceases to exist. In the Bible, it is said that life began when God breathed into Adam's nostrils. The breath we have has a rhythm and regularity. That rhythm regularizes our pulse, our heart beat and our nerves. Emotions such as anger change our rhythm, and affect the forces of Transport. Every time we move or exercise, this is an exercise in breath. Breath is a gateway for us to see the force of Transport in action, and a way to measure our regularity moment to moment.

Stay Lubricated

Smooth and agile motion is supported by lubrication. All machines move better when they are well lubricated. Think about it. Your car will not move without oil and regular oil changes. Neither will you. To support Transport, your body needs to be well lubricated. Lubrication supports our joints, enables cellular motion, lessens buildup of plaque in our arteries, and ensures that nerve impulses fire right.

Across a range of internal cellular processes, Transport needs lubrication. Without lubrication, the

272

machinery of our bodies begin to squeak, get tight, rust, and motion stops. That squeaking door in your kitchen needs some oil. The stiffness in your joints would also benefit from some lubrication. Lubrication removes friction and ensures long-life of machinery, including your inner machinery.

The right kinds of oils and fats, and proper hydration support that lubrication. Wonderful research is being done and continues to be done on the value of different kinds of wholesome plant and animal based fats and oils. Doing your own research on them can prove to be invaluable. Healthy fats and oils play an overall role in supporting the forces of Transport. They contribute to an increase in energy and help us gain muscle mass. They also support the functioning of our heart, lungs, brain and digestive organs --- all components involved in Transport. The right lubrication makes our internal motors of motion that move air, blood, electrical signals run with ease and minimal friction. Healthy fats help protect our heart, an important motor-like pump from cardiovascular diseases.

Our bones and skeletal structure keep us moving as we walk and run. Lubrication of the right kinds has been shown to strengthen bone density and reduce incidences of fractures, so as we age, we can still keep moving. Your skin is a major organ of transporting fluids and substances such as hormones, lymph, and water. Hydration, which is a form of lubrication, is key to supporting movement of those fluids and substance to support the forces of Transport.

The right kind of lubrication supports internal cellular signaling, and the right signaling is key to cellular communication. Wrong communication results in illness and disease. Repeated studies have shown the value of lubrication at the cellular level to protect against various forms of cancer. Lubrication protects our machinery from rusting --- a process known in chemistry as oxidation.

That bicycle chain in your backyard has oxidized and is rusty. Put some oil on it, clean it up, and it's as good as new. Similarly, oils that are known as anti-oxidants can help remove the "rust" from our internal motors so Transport forces are able to glide smoothly. Nerve signaling, a type of cellular signaling, affects mood disorders. Stress affects nerve signaling and may result in increased depression and anxiety. The right kind lubrication increases levels of serotonin in the body. Serotonin makes people feel good and puts them in a relaxed state. Being relaxed supports agile Transport.

Controlling the Forces of Conversion. Conversion is expressed as intensity and determination. When three key Inputs are present, Conversion presents itself as enterprising, brave, intelligent, ambitious, confident, and self-disciplined. These three Inputs are essential for Conversion to function at an optimal level: being cool, regulated and clean.

Stay Cool

Intensity doesn't need more intensity. Fighting fire with fire doesn't work here. The process of Conversion

274

does the job of converting Matter, Energy and Information from one form into another. These processes all require "heat." However, in order to operate efficiently, they also need proper cooling.

A nuclear reactor, which is able to convert nuclear fission to thermal energy, is a classic example of Conversion. But a nuclear reactor needs those big cooling towers we see when pictures of reactors are shown. Your hot kitchen needs an exhaust system to keep it cool; your computer needs a fan to keep it cool.

Men and women with rapid metabolism and fiery dispositions – expressions of Conversion in action -- need to stay cool, in both mind and body, to balance their internal engines. Those with Conversion dominance need to look to the external world for ways to input cooling factors. This is different from those with a Transport dominance, who need to Input ways of increasing internal warmth.

Conversion dominant people need to avoid "hot situations" that can cause tempers to flare; they need to learn to "cool down" during those times when the intensity of action (during tough business negotiations for example) becomes too extreme. Staying Cool ensures that you don't overheat and burn up your internal engines, which are the power source of Conversion.

Warm-blooded animals sweat (like a human) or pant (like a dog) to dissipate heat through water evaporation. Sometimes it's easy just to cool off by going under a nice shaded tree or get some water on us. Other times it may be good just to take a vacation, "chill out" and go to cooler areas. Sometimes just sitting and watching the

275

sunrise or sunset and other of Nature's beauty can serve to provide the cool to calm down and support the forces of Conversion, to remove the "heat."

Stay Regulated

The forces of Conversion are involved in the process of transformation and transduction. They convert energy from one form to another. The retinas in your eyes convert light, electromagnetic radiation, to chemical impulses which are transduced to "see" the world. The engine in your car converts chemical energy to rotational mechanical energy.

This all involves many systematic and interconnected processes that need to be regulated correctly, with great sensitivity, to make sure that the inputs are converted to the right outputs.

If your retina does not transduce correctly, you get a blurred vision. If your car engine's pistons are not regulated with the right mixture of fuel and air to fire correctly, your car's motion could be abrupt with backfiring. All engines need to regulate their activity from action to rest, from focused work to regular maintenance --- in short they need to be in balance across the forces of motion and stillness.

Conversion can create a tendency to push too hard. They gravitate toward being on the go all the time, with extreme activity and little rest. If they don't learn how to regulate their activities, they run the risk of "burning up" and "burning out". Sometimes, this inability to regulate their own internal engines, results in an attempt to control everything, and everybody, in their environment.

276

It would be better for them to learn how to control and regulate their own activities.

It can be difficult for a conversion dominant person to "let go" and relax with themselves and others. Their tongues can become harsh and mean --- an inappropriate way to control a situation, because in reality they are not able to control themselves. Extremes of this out-of-control behavior include throwing tantrums, becoming manipulative, all of which reflect a lack of self-regulation, which can backfire much like a car engine, whose internal pistons, misfire. High performance jet engines are designed to function well. They are able to operate across a wide range of temperatures and altitudes. They can regulate their engine performance across a variety of conditions, can adjust and adapt. Conversion forces require proper regulation to ensure their optimal functioning.

Regulation includes setting bounds of operation. Those who are dominated by Conversion forces can achieve great success if they are given, or create for themselves, internal and external boundaries. A high performance car also has its boundaries, if you "red-line" above a certain number of RPM's, the engine will conk out. The forces of Conversion operate well within their lower and upper bounds.

Work and rest are therefore equally important for these forces of Conversion. Forces of Conversion, like a motor can "be on" all the time, and not know when to stop. Men and women with strong Conversion forces have a tendency to overdo just about everything. They can work too hard, they can exercise too much, and they can over-do it with their attention to detail. Our Conversion dominant friends sometimes need to relax and stop competing. They need to learn to modulate their behavior, keeping everything more reasonable and moderate.

Regulating your behavior also implies being able to "surrender" and "go with flow" at appropriate times. Those with dominant Conversion forces can sometimes appear always to be on "high alert" in terms of a need to control the people and things in their environment. They need to learn how to regulate their behavior by stepping back and surrendering. It's essential to know when to stop, relax, rest, and shut down.

Stay Clean

Like any high performance engine, forces of Conversion thrive in a clean environment. This includes both high quality fuel and a clean internal mechanism. People dominated by Conversion need to be very careful about what they input into their bodies. Whole foods, organic and without preservatives, and without additives are wonderful because they provide "clean" fuel.

There is an emerging movement among pioneering food manufacturers in formalizing the definition of such clean foods through a newly developed Certified C.L.E.A.N. international standard, which I helped to facilitate using a systems-based approach that defines such foods as ones that have multiple attributes including being safe, non-GMO, organic, and having high bio-availability of nutrients. Keeping an eye out for such clean foods can serve to support Conversion.

Food combining is another wise strategy for ensuring effective transformation within our digestive systems. Slow-cooked foods, in many ways pre-digested, make it easy for our internal engine to absorb nutrients. In addition, regular and moderate fasts allow our engines to clean and heal themselves by support the body's own self-healing processes.

Controlling the Forces of Structure. Structure rings stability, and stability is essential for survival. Men and women in whom Structure is dominant tend to have stability in their own lives and they like to provide it for others as well. The three Inputs that encourage Structure's optimal performance are: being dry, active and flexible.

Stay Dry

The force of Structure provides containment and support. When a home is built, the foundation represents the Structure force that holds the entire house. If the foundation (or basement) is damp or wet, the building's entire infrastructure is at risk.

Excessive dampness in your body's foundation can show up as cysts, tumors, chronic sinus infections, and yeast infections. Dryness can also have the benefit of slightly raising the body's temperature, creating a structural environment that is resistant to viruses and bacteria. A dry sauna, for example, can be ideal for supporting Structure.

Stay Active

Use it or lose it. Any physical structure, including the human body, gets stronger the more it gets used and stimulated. If you don't use your muscles, your skeletal structure, you atrophy. Structures that are not used are vulnerable to decay and rust. Various types of stimuli are critical in keeping a structure activated.

At the cellular level, the cell membrane and cytoskeleton, supports structure of the entire cell. Nature ensures that this structure is under constant stimuli to keep it vigilant and active so it supports the cell structure. Such activity increases the number of macrophages. Macrophages enhance the immune system and support structure by killing invading bacteria and viruses.

Physical activity also increases blood flow, allowing antibodies to move through your system and attack and remove bacteria and viruses. For those who suffer from inflammation, anti-inflammatory cytokines, which are the cell-to-cell signaling molecules, are themselves activated by physical activity. These molecules have a beneficial effect in promoting anti-inflammatory effects. This is one of the important benefits that come from being active because chronic inflammation causes most of the degenerative diseases such as cancer.

The forces of Structure provide framework and inertia. This inertia can also result at its extremes in laziness, moodiness, and immobility. Sometimes those who are dominant in the forces of Structure "just don't feel like moving." Inertia and a lack of movement can contribute to a sense of depression or lethargy. Exercise and physical activity stimulates neurotransmitters in the brain to make one feel happier, less moody, and less depressed. Inertia is also implicated in osteoporosis, a structural disorder that causes bone loss. Exercise and physical activity is prescribed as a treatment for those who have osteoporosis or are in danger of getting it because it can help prevent and arrest the problem.

In order to hold things, Structure itself requires containment. The tendency to "holding on" often spells out issues with weight. Being active is a great controlling and modulating factor to manage one's weight. There is no better cure for the inertia and laziness of Structure forces than to boost one's energy level through physical activity. Diseases such as diabetes manifest when the forces of Structure go to its extremes of containment. Being active can be help deal with this condition. Activity helps makes the body more sensitive to insulin, to support burning of glucose e.g. calories. This helps to lower blood glucose and stop sugar spikes. Diabetics who exercise have been shown to need less insulin or medication than those who don't.

People with Structure dominance can also become too complacent and reliant on the status quo. They have a tendency to not want to "let go" of anything, including relationships and objects. They can "hold on" to relationships, situations, and things that no longer have value in their lives. Activity—getting out in the world, meeting new people, and trying new things—is a way of fighting this tendency.

Stay Flexible

Structure contains the elements of water and earth. Structures composed of water and earth can get stuck, muddy, swampy, and immobile. The most powerful structures in the world are not rigid, but flexible. If something is too hard, it can become brittle, and just shatter and break. In civil engineering, when larger structures are built, particularly in earthquake zones, they are designed to sway and to be flexible; sometimes they are even put on rollers, so they will move with the wave of the earthquake. The largest modern skyscrapers in the world now actually flex like pine grass in the wind.

This is a wonderful example of how flexibility can provide additional strength and make structures strong enough to withstand even the most powerful of Nature's forces. Similarly, flexibility is key for someone who is Structure dominant. If you become too stiff, you too can break or fall apart by life's continual and ongoing disturbances and changes. If you become too set in your ways, you might end up feeling as though you are stuck in a quagmire that resembles nothing so much as a muddy swamp.

Flexibility gives structures greater strength. Joints and fascia are particularly improved by flexibility. Blood flow can be increased by flexibility exercises such as stretching, which removes toxins and waste products that can cause a structure to "squeak" and get stiff.

Stretching the joints also results in improved blood flow, which, in turn, can cause slight increases in tissue temperature; this supports circulation and increases the flow of rich nutrients to the joints creating greater elasticity and higher levels of structural performance.

Flexibility allows structures to be more effective in dealing with environmental disturbances. My grandmother used to tell a story of two kinds of trees. One tree would bend when a river flooded and was able to go back to its original shape once the waters receded. The other tree would resist the flood and would ultimately be broken ripped out from its roots. Structures that bend are more likely to survive.

Scientists have repeatedly shown how flexible structures can adjust themselves to reduce drag. It is clear that that unlike rigid structures for which an increase in velocity causes a squared increase of drag, the increase in drag for a flexible object is significantly lower.

Above all, it's your responsibility – and your opportunity – to become fully aware of the dominant energies of your being, and your Goal is to keep them in balance to support your Natural System State, not someone else's. Remember too that balance is not a passive state. It's achieved through strong action, and strong action is required to sustain it as well. There's a teaching by Vivekananda, one of India's contemporary spiritual masters, that alludes to this. Despite his metaphysical orientation, Vivekananda advised his students that if there was a choice between doing 50 pushups or meditating for 50 minutes, do the pushups!

PART 5

What Is REAL Health?

CHAPTER 18

Life Is Dynamic, So Are You

With the combined wisdom of both ancient Siddha and modern systems theory on our side, we in the 21st century have a greater opportunity to create and maintain health than ever before in human history.

But what does health really mean? Is it a state of being, or a state of mind? Is it a clear x-ray, or a clear conscience, or some interdependent combination of both objective and subjective values?

Some years ago Dr. Deepak Chopra wrote a best selling book titled *Perfect Health*. Although that book was extremely successful in the marketplace, I have some serious issues with the title. Health is not a matter of perfection, and "perfect health" is a catchy but deceptive selling point. To use the analogy of a plane flight, health is an ongoing series of course corrections, some large and some small. The objective is always to stay in the air, not to arrive at some mythologically perfect location.

Life can move forward or backward, and health is a commitment to doing what it takes to move your life in the direction you want to go. Without commitment, health can't be sustained. Without the ability to course correct, the plane can't keep flying.

So far the focus of this book has been largely descriptive. We've described the reductionist approach to science, as well as the teachings of Siddha and the essentials of modern systems theory. In this final section we'll turn to a more prescriptive point of view. The reason is simple: in a book titled *Your Body, Your System* should do more than just show you a snapshot of who and what you are. It should show you how to become the person you want to be, even in the face of the inevitable obstacles and disturbances.

In systems terminology, your life and your health are (or should be) intelligent systems. You need to traverse the feedback loop of those on a continuous basis. That's the nature of intelligent systems, and resilience is the means of reaching goals through those systems.

Commitment means observing your Outputs. It means looking clearly at your goals and even refining them if necessary. You may need to remove or improve some of your Sensors. Make a commitment to knowing when that needs to happen and to getting it done. This will affect the forces of Transport, Conversion, and Structure within your consciousness and also in the physical realities of your life. Be prepared to making that happen and to embracing the results.

Altering Transport, for example, could mean that you'll need to move differently during the day. You

287

might need to move more quickly, or you might need to learn to sit still. Altering Transport could mean moving to a different house or apartment, or even to a different part of the country. Be ready to make that commitment when you first start using systems theory.

You may need to change the people who are around you in order to gain inspiration from friends. Or you may need to become more inspirational and proactive yourself. All this pertains to Transport.

Write down three examples of Transport that will be needed in order to attain your Goal? What are you going to need to change?

What about the forces of Conversion? Commit to identifying information from your Sensors and converting that information into action. You may not be able to do this entirely on your own. If you need an effective resume, you might not be a good enough writer to convert your education and experience into words on a page. So commit to finding someone who can help you with that conversion, or who can do it for you. You might need a good accountant or financial advisor. That may cost some money, so commit to paying what it costs. If you aren't happy with the first one you try, be resilient and find someone else.

Make a commitment also to building effective structure in your life. Structure doesn't mean rigidity. It's really a combination of strength and flexibility. A good way to start enhancing Structure in your life is to take up activities that support strength and flexibility in very physical ways. Anything from yoga to weight lifting can serve that purpose. Meditation and mindful practices can improve emotional and spiritual structure. Those activities require discipline, so make a commitment to supplying that discipline to the best of your ability.

CHAPTER 19

Resilience Across East & West

The active ingredient of commitment is resilience. In general terms, resilience is the ability to recover from adversity or successfully adapt to it. Psychiatrists and educators often use the word in discussing children who have experienced dysfunctional families or other forms of trauma. Environmentalists speak of the resilience of a region that has been subjected to droughts or major storms. Success and even survival demand resilience -- the power to dynamically reinvent yourself as circumstances change.

The Siddhars were keenly aware that the cosmos in which we live is itself a dynamic system, filled with multiple sub-systems, and that our individual systems could be affected by a wide range of environmental factors. The sun, solar flares, tides, pollution, phases of the moon, weather, dietary changes, current events, not to mention your family and friends, all have an impact on the system that is you. You are part of the cosmic soup, the environment that includes everything around you. That environment constantly affects you, and as you become more intuitive, you can learn to adjust the forces with your system to keep you on your path, in the midst of its dynamic changes and disturbances.

Airline pilots know that they are going to be off-course as much as 95% of the time. However, they receive second-by-second feedback from their instruments, and control their systems by making constant adjustments to the Inputs of altitude, speed, and fuel consumption in order to fly thousands of miles, traversing multiple time zones, geographies, weather conditions, and oceans before making near perfect landings--- an incredible feat of feedback and control in action!

Siddhar masters were similarly adept at knowing how to tell whether someone's system was on and off course. They knew what things looked like when they were operating right, and they also knew what things looked like when things were not operating right. Just like the pilot who observes his/her instrument panel, Siddhars, like my grandmother, could observe your face and in an instant know what was "off course". Our journey across Siddha and Systems Biology, now unravels this magic to find out when we are off course, using our new found understanding of Nature's forces.

Knowing your Natural System State and the Inputs that drive it, is a major leap forward on that journey. You have been empowered to take care of your physical vessel through fundamental principles. This is an important aspect of both Siddha and Systems Biology.

Now, you are ready to take the next leap forward by mastering the art of how to navigate your system under disturbances. This will test your knowledge of principles, and also motivate you to connect across both the visible and invisible worlds in order to become adept at adjusting to those changes.

In order to accomplish this, two key things are necessary:

>> **Feedback:** Becoming aware of the current state of your system. This awareness lets us answer the question: How am I actually doing now, this moment? The answer to this question helps you to know your current system state. Without this, you will not know whether you are "on-course" or "off-course".

>> **Adjustment:** Based on the current system state and where we want to go (our goal), adjustment involves making decisions on what Inputs to focus on, to resilient;y put our systems on the right trajectory.

When we connect the dots across East and West --- across both systems -- this is what we discover. The terms Natural Systems State and Prakriti are one and the same --- your body's *homeostasis* as western biology teaches us. The Disturbed State (when you are off course) and the Vikriti are one and the same --- when your body is in *allostasis*, a term also known to western biologists. Allostasis is a state that your body goes into

292

when it is under constant stress. You may think this is a normal state if you are in it long enough. But it is not. That leads to chronic disease.

The key is to bring your body back to homeostasis, back to your Natural Systems State, back to its Prakriti.

How do you do this? Simple, you learn to sit still and listen.

Our bodies always know the truth and they are always speaking to us. The problem is most of us do not ask for this feedback, nor do adjust if we do happen to listen. Listening is the best way to get the feedback we need.

The following are two very powerful approaches for listening to what your inner self already knows. Another word for this is meditation.

Method One: Connecting Through Breath and Sensation

Over the past four decades, my research and education also involved exploring a wide range of practices to experience various aspects of the inner worlds. These practices work across the range of our Nadis, Koshas, and Chakras. Some enable us to develop the powers of visualization to manifest our goals and desires.

When I was very young, my grandparents initiated me to one of the ancient Siddha practices of the Third Eye, which involved using mantras and visualizations in order to manifest goals. By the time I was 14, I became adept at this. While these practices made me realize the immense power each one of us has to achieve anything we wish, something felt unfulfilled. My journey took me to explore other methods.

I experienced Nada Yoga and Surat Shabd Yoga, which enabled me to connect to the inner Koshas using sound and light vibrations to travel inward. These are very powerful techniques, and the experiences were magical. From these techniques, one realizes the power of vibration and that sound and light are manifestations of our internal vibrational states. However, there was a heavy emphasis on getting to the next "state", having the next inner experience.

Other meditative approaches such as Transcendental Meditation offered very powerful ways to connect deep using a Mantra and sound. Such techniques were also very powerful when used appropriately.

Over the years, however, I have come to value a very simple approach, which is perhaps the simplest, and in my opinion, and the most powerful approach to connect within, go inward, and above all build an ultimate sense of awareness that awakens the ability to get feedback on the sensations and condition of the mind and body.

That approach is simply through mindful observation of breath and sensations. We begin by observing our natural breathing, and then observing the sensations of the body. Simple, but amazingly powerful. Hundreds of research papers have shown how stress is lowered and released through meditative and relaxation practices. Such research points to the up and down regulation of various proteins in our bodies, demonstrating the positive effects of such practices at the molecular level. However, remember, that stillness practices such as these are also medicine, and need to be used appropriately.

The practice of mindful observation becomes a powerful tool for us to traverse across Matter and Energy to the source of all Information. Blocks in our energy network, our Nadis and Chakras, need to be addressed to support our inner journeys as well as our physical and mental health.

This ancient approach of the Siddhars was referenced in various forms throughout the ages. Buddha 2,500 years ago referred to it as Vippassana, which meant "seeing things as they truly are." The modern Siddha master Satyananda Saraswati developed this approach into the powerful technique known as Yoga Nidra. Fundamental to both these methods were the equanimous observation of breath and sensations.

Remember, everything should personalized. If you are Structure dominant, and are prone to want to be "still", then before you begin this practice, it is advised that you do it after vigorous activity of some sort. That will have a balancing effect.

Start with Your Natural Breath

The technique is simple. You can begin by setting your clock for 15 minutes. Find a quiet place indoors that is comfortable. Sit straight. If you want to do a yoga posture, do so, but it's not necessary. Begin by closing your eyes. Your mantra is not a sound, as you would get during initiation from a yoga Master, but YOUR BREATH. YOUR BREATH is your mantra. Begin by simply observing your natural breath. Do not try to change it, move it, get concerned about the rate of your breath, if one nostril is

295

breathing, or even if you stop --- simply observe your natural breath. Observe the flow, in and out. Simply observe, without any judgement. If there are disturbances in your environment, dog barking, thoughts, itches, etc., simply acknowledge them, and quietly bring your attention back to your breath. This breath is YOU. It is your Prana moving through you. Your observation of the breath will begin the process of connecting you to YOU.

Now Observe Sensations in Your Body

Recall our Architecture of You. In this process of observing the sensations, we will move progressively from the more gross worlds of Matter to the more subtle worlds of Energy. We traverse our Temple Within. We do this by first learning to observe sensations of the outer layers of our bodies, the Annamaya Kosha, the skin, again from head to toe, toe to head. Then as we get more adept, we can move our attention to observe the sensations in the superficial fascia, the area right below our skin, the second Kosha, or Pranamaya Kosha, then onward to the third layer, the myofascia, the fascia surrounding our muscles, which maps to the Manomaya Kosha, the causal body. The fourth layer is the deep fascia, surrounding our organs, which maps to the Vijnanamaya Kosha, the etheric body. The fifth layer is the cellular fascia surrounding our cells, which maps to the Anandamaya Kosha, the soul body. We use our power of visualization and imagination to see these layers and move our consciousness across them, layer by layer, head to toe, toe to head, and simply observe with equanimity the sensations on the body.

As you practice, your sensitivity will become more refined, and be become more aware of how you react and respond to events in your environment, within and

296

without. Such awareness builds your own "sense" of YOU and sensitizes your Feedback mechanism. This method builds your "core strength" at a very deep level, and supports the development of your own feedback intuition.

Method Two: Self-Questioning of Your Current State

This is a self-reflective version of the Socratic Method: ask yourself questions. You may chose to use this self-questioning approach either in conjunction with or separate from Method One.

Your instrument here is your own ability to assess how the forces of Nature are manifesting themselves within us. Systems Biology is moving eventually towards building advanced diagnostic tests, which one day will automate this for us --- and likely more achievable by incorporating the systems concepts of Siddha. In this method, you ask yourself which forces of Transport, Conversion or Structure are "off-course" in your system at this moment, based on the disturbances you are facing.

The answers to those questions today may be different than tomorrow – but that is to be expected, life is dynamic. When your system is stressed by disturbances in your own life, it reacts quickly by sending out cues to alert you that you need to make some adjustments.

Adjustments, can only take place if you know that you are "off-course." Most people don't even know if they are off course. In the case of the airplane, if we want to maintain an altitude of 30,000 feet, the altimeter will tell us in real-time, how far off we are. In life, it is difficult sometimes, to know how we are off, especially if we have become habitual to being off-course.

But when you know your Natural System State and how the forces of Transport, Conversion and Storage coalesce for you individually you can use self-inquiry to discover when there are perturbations or deviations in these forces. From a systems standpoint, you need to know which is force is off-course, so you can adjust. Is your Transport off? Is your Conversion off? Is your Storage off? This is no different than the pilot asking himself is my altitude off? Is my speed off? Is my direction off?

When you've asked and answered these systems-related questions about your current state and the disturbances you're facing, you can continue with other questions that relate more specifically to your daily life. These can reveal areas of emotional vulnerability that can translate into physical issues. By bringing clarity to how you're feeling, the questions and answers can also strengthen resilience.

CHAPTER 20

Simple, But (Maybe) Not Easy

The ability to bounce back is stronger in some people than in others. But you can strengthen your resilience just like you can build up your muscles or your bank account. Your opportunity – and your responsibility -- is to maximize that capacity in your life every day.

Certain conditions in your life can help you to be resilient. The more resources you have to recover strongly from problems and setbacks, the more resilient you will be. As you read the questions below, a "yes" answer indicates that resource is available to you. When you answer no, think about what changes you need to make and how you plan to make them.

One: Do you have people in your life who will listen to you attentively and give you honest feedback, without being judgmental or personally critical?

Two: Beyond specific individual relationships, are you involved in any organization -- a church or school, for example – that can be a resource for support and information?

Three: Are you in good health and decent physical condition? Do you avoid unhealthy food and drink? Are you getting enough sleep and exercise?

Four: Do you have people in your life who believe in you unconditionally, from whom you receive encouragement and positive reinforcement?

Five: Regardless of what others may think, do you have faith in yourself? Do you feel generally optimistic about your ability to accomplish your goals even when you encounter disturbances?

Six: Do you feel that your opinions and your decisions are heard and valued in your personal relationships? What about in your work and career?

Seven: Do you volunteer to help others in your community and in the world? This can mean donating your time through a community or spiritual organization -- or it can involve charitable financial donations on a regular basis?

Eight: Do most of your relationships with friends and family members have clear boundaries -- providing mutual respect, personal independence, and both giving

300

and receiving on the part of each person? Do you set and maintain boundaries for yourself -- by saying "no" when you need to?

Nine: Would you describe yourself as a generally optimistic person, or as more of a pessimist? On the whole, do you believe things have a tendency to work out for the best -- or do you think problems have a tendency to persist and grow larger?

If you answered yes to a majority of those questions, you seem to have a strong support system in various areas of your life. These are people and organizations you can rely on when you need them. Along with external resources, people also overcome difficulties through internal qualities.

What follows below can be thought of as a "personal resiliency list." Probably no one possesses all the elements on this list. You may have three or four of these qualities that you use most naturally and most often. Still, you may never have clearly identified these attributes in your own mind. It's useful to recognize your primary resiliency builders, and it's also important to develop new ones to the greatest possible extent.

There are seven personal resiliency builders. As you hear each one described, ask yourself whether it's a very strong presence in your life, just average, or a relatively weak area that you could probably develop.

We can call the first quality "sociability." How good are you at being a friend and in forming positive relationships?

The second trait is humor. This doesn't mean you tell jokes all the time. It's means seeing the comical element in life. It also means being able to laugh at yourself even in serious circumstances.

The third trait is insight. Do you think you have above average understanding of people and situations? Do you feel that you often see things that others miss?

Number four is called "adaptive distancing." Are you generally able to recognize negative people and situations, and to keep your distance from them?

The fifth trait is flexibility. How well do you adjust to change? Are you able to bend but not break in challenging situations?

Trait six is personal competence. Is there something that you're really good at -- something that gives you renewed self-confidence and energy?

The seventh trait, which is probably the most important of all for resilience, is perseverance. How well are you able to keep on trying despite difficulty? Do you tend give up pretty quickly? Or slowly? Or never?

My intention for this book was to show the connections between East and West, between body and mind, between esoteric teachings of science and spirituality and straightforward common sense.

There is of course much more for you to learn about Your Body, Your System -- and I hope you've found this book to be a good start in the right direction.

VOLUME 3

Your System Your Life

MIT Engineer's Guide To The Ultimate System
For Achieving Any Goal You Choose

INTRODUCTION

I'm an engineer by training, and engineers are workhorses. We get things done. Engineers build things, whether it's new bridges or new molecules.

What will you learn to build in this book? You're going to learn to build the life you want using state of the art principles of systems theory, one of the most exciting and advanced areas of modern science. Here at the start, of course, you have every right to ask about my credentials for such an ambitious project. When someone says they can show you how to achieve any goal you choose, you shouldn't believe them unless they've achieved some significant things themselves. I certainly would not believe them. So let me tell you a bit about myself.

My credentials include four degrees, including a Ph.D. from the Massachusetts Institute of Technology (M.I.T.). But that's only part of why I am qualified to write a book about achieving any goal you choose.

Let me tell you where I come from. I was born into a lower caste family in Mumbai, the most populous city in India. For people in the West, it's difficult to imagine exactly how different that point of origin is from the settings in which most of my highly credentialed colleagues grew up. It really was a different planet. In many ways it was disadvantaged, but it also provided me with an emotional and spiritual foundation that has served me well. I'll have more to say about that in the pages that follow.

My family moved to New Jersey when I was seven years old and I quickly distinguished myself in public school. I had a highly competitive nature and I wanted to do well in everything. I would stay up late at night doing math problems, and I would practice pitching a baseball against a wall for hours on end.

At age fourteen I completed a special program in computer technology at NYU's Courant Institute of Mathematical Science. I was then recruited by the University of Medicine and Dentistry of New Jersey as a Research Fellow. This led to an experience that would change my life forever and – I can honestly say this – it would change the world as well.

My mentor at UMDNJ presented me with a seemingly impossible challenge that, given my competitive nature, was irresistible to me. I was asked to create a computerized equivalent of the time-honored interoffice mail system, in which hard copies of documents were circulated through an office environment in large manila envelopes.

This happened at a time when the role of computers in average people's lives was basically non-existent. If anyone heard of Bill Gates' mission statement for Microsoft – to put a personal computer in every home in America – it would have sounded like a complete fantasy, like saying that everyone would walk on the moon.

But I didn't know about how impossible it all was, and if I had, I wouldn't have cared. I was on a mission. It wasn't only about meeting the challenge that had been set for me as an individual. I wanted to make life easier for all the office workers I saw typing up hard copies of documents to put in envelopes. In India, I had seen the reality of hard and tedious physical labor. Now I saw myself as someone on a mission to create a change that would revolutionize the lives of the people around me.

I wrote fifty thousand lines of computer code for a user-friendly communication software program that included inbox, outbox, attachments, folders, and all the other features of email. But there was no "email" until then. At that hospital in Newark, I literally invented email. I even got a U.S. government copyright on my software system, which I named "EMAIL." Copyright was the only legal protection available for software at that time. Don't take my word for it. Google me. Ask "Who invented email?"

I'm not telling you this to blow my own horn. I want you to see what can be accomplished when there's motivation, determination, a worthwhile goal, and training. Imagine seeing a five or six year old boy in rural India and saying, "Well, in ten years that boy will invent the most revolutionary communications technology since the telephone." Would that have seemed like a realistic goal? Would that have seemed even remotely possible? Yet that's what happened. If that can happen in my life, I can assure you that your goals, no matter how far out they may seem, are also within your grasp.

For the next thirty-three years I sought neither recognition nor financial gain for my invention of email. I started many companies whose clients included the Clinton White House, Nike, Calvin Klein, and many others. I was retained by the government of India to oversee and evaluate the state of scientific innovation in that country. I have been an entrepreneur as well as a scientist, and along the way I made a significant amount of money.

Then, in 2011, an article appeared in Time magazine entitled "The Man Who Invented Email." Soon the Smithsonian wanted the papers documenting my invention of email from 1978. On February 16, 2012, the Washington Post printed an article with the headline, "V.A. Shiva Ayyadurai Honored by Smithsonian as the Inventor of Email."

That's when something happened that I – quite naively – had not expected. The fact that I was an outsider, that I came from the periphery and had then achieved success in mainstream universities and businesses, had been taken as an affront by the high tech "geek" establishment. They were waiting to pounce. My work was suddenly scandalizing to the denizens of academia and the military-industrial complex that has historically claimed ownership to all major innovations. On internet tabloids I was called a "liar" and a "fraud."

But here's what really got the goat of the tech insiders. When I was ridiculed and defamed, I did not humbly fade away. I wouldn't, and I couldn't, conform to the reassuring Mahatma Gandhi stereotype. I would not obligingly let myself be sacrificed like Gunga Din and sit in the lotus position. In short, I was not willing to be a "good Indian."

How infuriating that was to industry elites! But the people who were infuriated had not spent their early years as a low caste "untouchable" in Mumbai. They had not moved from Mumbai to Paterson, New Jersey. They had not gotten recognition from the Smithsonian, and then abruptly been called a liar and a fraud. If anything like that had happened to them, I'm sure they would feel the same way I did.

Over time I've come to see how real innovators, especially if they don't have a conventional pedigree, have always been threatening to the established power structure. I've seen how people who had new goals and original ideas have always had to overcome obstacles. An important part of achieving your goals will be dealing with people who want to stop you from achieving them, and who will resent you when you do.

Whatever my own challenges have been, I'm eager to share with you what I've learned from those challenges. Most importantly, I want give you the practical tools and techniques I've learned so that you can achieve your own goals, regardless of any obstacles you encounter. Once again, as when I was challenged to invent email, I feel

311

like I've been given an assignment. My assignment is to tell you a secret truth – that you can achieve any goal you want -- and if you don't believe me, if you doubt me, I have to change your mind.

What is that secret truth? It's the theory and practice of systems. Those words may mean nothing to you now, but that's about to change. But let me be clear: I am not going to tell you to spend all day meditating or to switch to a probiotic diet. Those things have their value, but there will be serious work required here in order to complete the process of reaching the goals you set for yourself. Fair warning! But if you're willing to do what it takes, you can not only get what you want, but you can do more than you ever imagined. And remember, I'm saying that as someone who came from rural India to create a world-changing revolutionary innovation. If I can do it so can you.

This book is a part of the Systems Health® series. In *The Science of Everything*, I provide my journey as a scientist to discover a core scientific foundation that allows you to understand any system in the world. That discovery emerged from my interconnecting the knowledge systems of eastern medicine with modern control systems theory. In *The System and Revolution*, I provide a systems approach to understand what is revolution and to expose some of the erroneous myths of modern science that subjugate our rational thinking. The book *Your Body, Your System* focuses on your body as a system to reveal how you can use systems principles to not only support your health but also, and more importantly to use your body as a laboratory to understand the principles all systems in the universe.

In Part One of this book you'll learn the fundamentals of systems theory, including the startling fact that everything is a system. This is a principle that modern science is just beginning to articulate. Yet it has been understood by indigenous wisdom traditions around the world for thousands of years. In particular, as you will learn in these pages, the Indian system of physical and spiritual health known as Siddha anticipates and in some areas surpasses Western approaches to physical, mental and spiritual health and achievement.

In Part Two, you'll learn about four real world examples that clarify exactly how systems theory can be applied to setting goals and attaining them. These are narratives of people who got what they wanted by following an engineering systems approach. What the goal might be is much less important than seeing how systems theory can be applied to it. That's why it's important to grasp how the application of systems principles works in a variety of real world settings.

In Part Three, you'll see how you can get started right away by using your own body as a system to serve as a proving ground and resource for applying systems theory, in a very practical way, so it's not just theory. Yes, this will benefit your health – but for our purposes here it will be just as important for to see how a systems approach works in your unique and highly individualized state of physical being. You'll learn what the real goal of health is and how to apply the principles of systems theory to modulate the inputs to achieve that goal.

Then, in Part Four, you'll have a chance to choose a goal in your life, and see how, in a step by step manner, it can be achieved by using the science of systems.

All of this will provide you the keys to understand a universal set of principles that span modern science and the ancient wisdom of Siddha, to achieving any goal. I know that's a big promise, but there are powerful tools waiting for you to turn that promise into a reality.

Let's get started.

PART 1

Systems Theory: The Foundation for Achieving Any Goal

CHAPTER 1

The Five Principles of All Systems

The best way to achieve your goals is through the science of systems or systems theory, and you're about to learn exactly what systems theory really is. It's definitely not dry or academic. Systems theory is extremely practical and down to earth. We'll even explain it using everyday examples from around the house.

A system is a set of objects or energies working together for a specific goal or purpose. The first step toward understanding systems theory is recognizing the connections between elements that might once have seemed separate but are actually linked together in a system.

To a child, for example, an acorn seems like a completely independent object. It's inconceivable to a child that a tiny acorn could actually be part of a vast system of oak trees covering years of time and acres of space. As we get older, systems become more recognizable. Connections that were invisible begin to reveal themselves, especially when we start to look for those connections.

Systems can be simple or infinitely complex. A wristwatch, a cow, a human heart, a city, and a washing machine are all systems – as is the Earth itself and even the whole universe. Your body is a system with many subsystems within it. Once you understand how systems work, you can understand how anything works.

To achieve any goal, you will need to understand how *intelligent systems* function. But before we go there, we will begin by understanding how open systems work. Open systems are a subset or a part of all intelligent systems. Understanding the principles of open systems is the immediate task or goal at hand.

A toaster and an electric heater, as you will find out shortly, are examples of open systems. But the presence of a thermostat makes your home heating system an intelligent system.

All open systems have five basic elements: *Input, Output, Transport, Conversion, and Structure* as shown in Figure 1. An intuitive understanding of these five basic elements will provide the foundation for understanding intelligent systems.

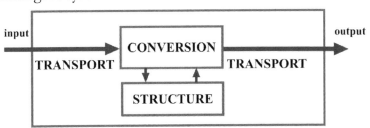

Figure 1 – Open system in modern systems theory.

Input: Input is the stuff coming into a system. There can be a single input or multiple inputs. An input can be information, matter, or energy. For example, what did you have to eat today? Did you get any exercise, or did you stay in bed all afternoon? What did you see out the window? What music did you listen to? Whom did you speak with on the phone?

The answers to all those questions comprise today's input for the system that is you. Emotion, nutrition, material wealth, spirituality, physical comfort or the lack of it – these elements, and many more, constitute the input of matter or energy or information that moves your life forward toward achieving your goals, or backward away from them.

No one can have total control over all the inputs in life. But we can be mindful of those inputs. We can become conscious of them, and we can make changes to those inputs in the direction of our goals. Our life's inputs, which are the actions we take, are called *karma* in the Siddha tradition of India. Karma literally means the actions --- the sum total of everything that we input into our physical, emotional, and spiritual selves as well as into the world around us.

Output: Output is the stuff coming out of a system. This can be a single output or multiple outputs and, like input, output can be information, matter, or energy. The output is the direct result of the inputs (the karma) into a system. If you somehow plugged your toaster into a nuclear power plant, there would be too much electrical input. This would cause a negative output: your toaster

318

blows up. But if you try to light a city with flashlight batteries, you'll get a negative output for the opposite reason: too little input. Depending on the situation, not enough can be as bad as too much.

Sometimes it's easy to connect a cause with an effect – to connect an input (karma) with the resulting output, the fruits of one's action --- known as *karma-phal* (the fruits of karma --- the fruits our action) in the Siddha wisdom tradition. More often, recognizing cause-and-effect, input-and-output, may take some insight and focused attention. Why did you feel especially energetic today? Is it because you got a good night's sleep, or because you drank three cups of strong coffee? Why did you feel angry? Why did you fall in love?

To answer those questions, you need to be mindful of whether you did feel energetic or angry, and if you did fall in love. Those feelings and experiences are the outputs, the results of your actions, of your karma. Are those outputs the ones you want? Are they the realization of your goals, or something very different?

Transport: This is the principle of *movement* in a system: the process of information, matter, or energy moving from input to output, from karma to *karma-phal*, from cause to effect. It's the presence or absence of dynamic progress of stuff moving from source to destination. In a computer, transport is the aspect of the machine's process of moving information, bits of ones and zeroes, through the system, from the keyboard (input) to the screen display (output). When purchasing a computer, you may want one that does this very quickly, or you may need to focus on something else.

When the principle of transport is dominant in a person's system, short-term bursts of creativity, financial income, or emotional stimulation can happen, but longer-term stability may need more attention.

It's the difference between comfort and speed. There's nothing wrong with the fundamental nature of a really fast sports car. It's just that you shouldn't use one for towing a heavy trailer. Or if you do, you should become good friends with your mechanic.

In the Siddha tradition, the principle of transport is called *vata*, and it is associated with natural phenomena such as the wind. Like the wind, transport can be forceful or mild, fast or slow, but changeability is its essential feature.

Visual images can enable you to develop an intuitive understanding of Transport. When a dancer leaps and floats through the air, she expresses the energy of transport.

The cars buzzing along a busy highway are transport in action.

Your body *transports* food through your digestive system.

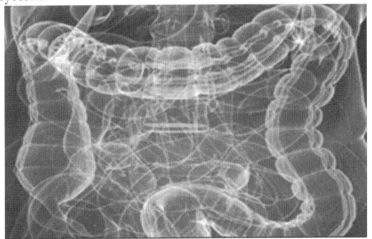

Conversion: In systems theory, conversion refers to the process of transforming or *converting* an Input into an Output. The force of conversion changes information, matter, or energy from one form to another. The Central Processing Unit (CPU) of a computer, along with the necessary software, embodies conversion. When you

321

input three symbols on the keyboard: "1 + 1" -- the CPU converts those symbols into an output, which is "2."

Think of a supersonic fighter plane. The force of conversion is expressed by the jet engines, where fuel is converted to thrust. In a fighter plane speed is critical, so the plane quickly consumes fuel. A fighter plane can burn an enormous amount of fuel in order to achieve maximum speed for a short period of time.

The principle of conversion manifests in every area of our lives, from processing information to recovering from the breakup of an emotional relationship to converting food into energy. In the Siddha system, conversion is known as *pitta*.

A leaf manifests the principle of conversion when photosynthesis uses sunlight to convert carbon dioxide, water, and minerals into organic matter and oxygen.

A steel mill converts iron ore into molten steel, which is then further converted into a finished product.

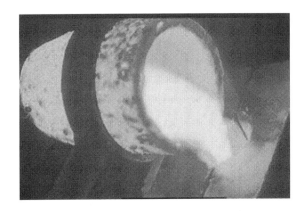

Structure: The structure of a system refers to the boundaries, connections, and overall internal environment <u>within</u> which the activities of transport and conversion take place. Structure is sometimes referred to as the storage aspect of a system. A car, whether it's a racer or a SUV, needs a body or frame made of metal, rubber, and plastic. Both a fighter jet and a passenger plane need the fuselage, which holds the cockpit, seats, and engines. Health, physical strength, and emotional stability are structural aspects of a human system. In Siddha, the structure or storage element is referred to as *kapha*.

When a bullet is shot from a rifle, the barrel of the rifle provides the structure for the bullet to propel toward the target. The bullet itself is also an example of structure. It provides the Structure to contain gunpowder, which is the explosive used to propel the bullet. When the rifle is fired, both the bullet and the barrel become structural elements of the same system.

Just as a bullet provides structure for the energy of the gunpowder, a battery is a structure to store electrical energy.

Every cell includes the structure of the cell wall or cell membrane to contain all the contents of the entire cell.

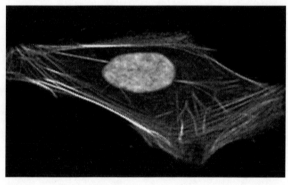

Bones provide structure for securing the body's organs and muscles.

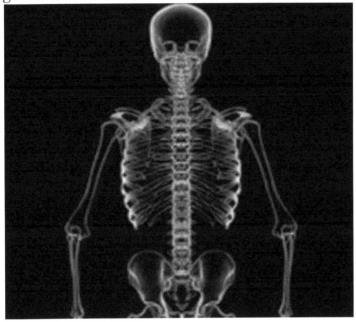

To review, in modern systems theory, the five elements we've discussed are referred to as Input, Output, Transport, Conversion and Structure. In the ancient Siddha tradition, the same principles are known as Karma, Karma-Phal, Vata, Pitta, and Kapha, respectively.

These principles that are central to modern science and engineering have been recognized and have remained constant for more than 5,000 years, when the great Siddhars (sages) expressed them. Table 1 summarizes this terminology across both systems of knowledge from modern systems theory to ancient Siddha.

Modern Systems Theory	Siddha
Input	Karma
Output	Karma-Phal
Transport	Vata
Conversion	Pitta
Structure (or Storage)	Kapha

Table 1 – Modern systems theory and Siddha.

A diagram of an open system, therefore, using the language of Siddha is shown in Figure 2.

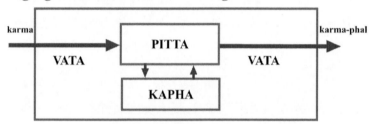

Figure 2 – Open system in Siddha.

CHAPTER 2

Open Systems

An open system is one that provides a particular Output from a particular Input. Once the Input is set, the Output is defined.

A water faucet is a simple example of an open system. Turn the handle clockwise to a particular location (the Input) and water flows out at a certain rate (the Output) from wherever it was stored in the

Structure of the pipes, and is Transported out of the spigot. Water keeps coming out of the spigot until you turn the handle to its original OFF position. The Conversion element is the valve, which serves to stop and start the transport of water.

A basic electric room heater is another everyday example of an open system. Assuming the heater is plugged into the wall, turning the heater ON and setting it to a particular level – the Inputs of LOW, MEDIUM or HIGH -- results in a certain amount of heat, which is the Output. Transport is the process of transporting electric current from the wall socket in to the heater, as well as the heat from the heating coils into the room. Conversion, represented by the heating coils, is what transforms the electrical energy into heat or thermal energy. The Structure element is the entire unit that contains all the components of the system.

Once the machine is turned ON, and set at a particular level, the heater will continue taking in electricity at that particular level and sending out heat without any self-regulation. It will keep working at the same rate until it is turned OFF. Later, we will see how this heater, an open system, can be converted to an intelligent system in which the Input can dynamically vary to get different Output of heat.

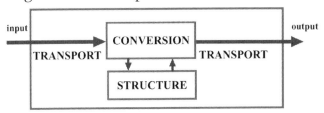

Figure 3 – Faucet and heater are both open systems.

In summary, the faucet and heater are both examples of an open system consisting of the five basic elements as shown in Figure 3. They take in an input and give an output. Table 2, below, summarizes the five specific elements relevant to these two types of open systems.

	Faucet	**Heater**
Input	Handle position of faucet	ON/OFF switch, and heating level: Low, Medium or High
Output	Rate of Flow of Water	Heat
Transport	Flow of water	Flow of electric current and heat
Conversion	Valve that converts handle position into amount of flow	Heating coils that convert electrical current and the level setting to heat
Structure	The pipes that store water	The heating unit that contains the heating coil and electrical components

Table 2– The five elements of a faucet and heater.

All open systems take in an Input and produce a specific Output. One underlying assumption of open systems is that the Output maintains itself as long as the Input is maintained.

Human beings can also be open systems – and there's nothing wrong with that, provided that it's a conscious choice. The assumption is, for example, you show up to work, work hard and you get as Output a steady income, a stable relationship, and security --- all of which are worthwhile desires. They are certainly what most people hoped for and wanted during much of American history.

But now life is more fluid, unstable and improvisational. Change happens faster. It's no longer easy to even imagine what things were like before laptops and cellphones, even though they've only been around for a relatively short time.

So let's be clear about the relationship between the Input and Output in open systems. An open system provides for a stable and predictable result that is as close to being guaranteed as it can possibly be. If external disturbances occur that affect the result --- the Output --- open systems are not capable of self-correction or self-regulation to adjust the system in order to obtain the original Output.

And once again, there's nothing wrong with getting predictable results from well-understood and conventional actions, provided it's what you really want. But that's becoming more difficult in a world where rapid change is the norm. New technologies and historical changes are demanding that we be more flexible and resilient. For survival and success in that world, an open system existence might no longer be the best choice.

CHAPTER 3

Intelligent Systems

In systems theory, the really powerful systems are *intelligent systems* --- also called feedback or closed loop systems. They work differently. Intelligent systems include four additional elements: a Goal; Disturbances; a Sensor; and, a Controller. These elements enable self-regulation and continuous adjustment of the Input in order to achieve a desired Output that matches the Goal. Through the use of a Sensor and a Controller, this can be achieved in spite of Disturbances to the system.

Figure 4 provides a diagram of an intelligent system using the language of modern systems theory:

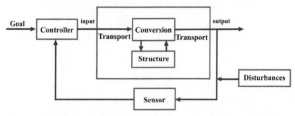

Figure 4 – Intelligent system, from modern systems theory, "closes the loop" of the open system to achieve the Goal by

using the Sensor to sense the difference between the Output and the Goal to allow the Controller to change the Input.

In Figure 4, notice that the open system is now a subset of the intelligent system. Unlike the open system, an intelligent system begins with a Goal, an intention, (or a *Dharma* or *Sankalpa* as they are referred to in Siddha). Setting this Goal is your responsibility and the Goal must be chosen wisely. The entire process of being "intelligent" exists to achieve that Goal, in spite of any Disturbances that occur.

Disturbances are those things that get in the way of achieving our Goal. They can be physical obstacles, or procrastination, inability to focus, and poor eating habits. In Siddha, obstacles were known as *Vikaras*. The ancient Siddhars meticulously itemized all the known Vikaras a human may face in a lifetime.

But, here is the *real* secret to achieving a Goal. First, we must use and refine our *Sensors* to know the current Output --- where we are at right now. Then we should use and develop our *Controller* to measure the difference between where we want to go --- our Goal, and our Output. The Controller is the "brains" to strategically figure out a new Input to affect the forces of Transport, Conversion and Structure to get a desired Output, so we can move closer to our Goal. And, this process occurs over time as we go around the loop, and each time getting closer to our Goal.

As shown in Figure 4, we do this by "closing the loop" of the open system, by feeding back the Output of the open system to a Sensor, which is used to measure the actual Output. In the Siddha tradition, the Sensor was known as the *Indriyas* of the human body --- the Indriyas were our literal senses of smell, touch, sight, taste and hearing. How well the Sensor can measure is critical to knowing exactly where we are. A poor Sensor can give us an erroneous measure of the Output, and this will affect the decisions of the Controller. In Siddha, the purpose of awareness practices such as meditation, yoga and other spiritual activities was to enhance one's Indriyas (sensors). The more our sensors are refined, the closer one can get to the Goal or Sankalpa.

The Controller (or *Manas* in Siddha) literally measures the difference between our Goal and the actual Output to make a decision on what new Input (or Karma) we need to send back into the system to affect changes in the forces of Transport (Vata), Conversion (Pitta) and Structure (Kapha), to get a new Output (Karma-Phal). Figure 5 demonstrates how intelligent systems appear from a Siddha standpoint.

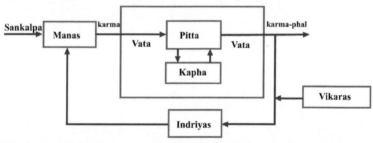

Figure 5 – Intelligent system, from Siddha, "closes the loop" of the open system to achieve the Sankalpa by using the Indriyas to sense the difference between the Karma-Phal and the Sankalpa to allow the Manas to change the Karma.

The Controller element is perhaps the most important aspect of intelligent systems. The Controller is all about making decisions. By integrating the Goal with information coming in from the Sensors, the Controller makes decisions that result in actions, which are new Inputs into the system. These Inputs result in the Transport and Conversion of information, matter, and energy within a Structure, which leads to a new Output. As the sequence takes place and we become aware of the Output from our actions, the Controller draws on this awareness to make a subsequent decision. This results in a new Input. Based on that new Input, the process of Transport and Conversion of information, matter, and energy within a Structure is reiterated and refined.

When Disturbances are encountered, the system must course-correct back toward the Goal. Because this is a continuous process, it's critical that awareness and information – and the decisions that result – can be made on the fly. The more refined our awareness becomes by developing our Sensors, the better our decisions will be. For this reason, spiritual practices, which promote stillness and refinement of our awareness --- the Sensors, enable a clearer perception of what is really taking place and to see the Output with accuracy as it really is. This in turn allows the Controller to make better decisions. When in doubt, therefore, it's important to be still and refine your awareness.

Rather than a strictly spiritual approach, this is a principle of modern systems theory. It is also the essence of Siddha, which teaches stillness as a path to awareness, right decisions, and right action – which together result in the Output of achieving the Goal we desire. In both systems theory and Siddha, this process is what intelligence really means.

At any point in life, we can simply be reactive to what's happening around us, or we can set and approach our goals based on awareness, intention, and intelligence.

Every journey begins with a Goal and some level of awareness. As our awareness becomes more refined, our Controller can make decisions that translate the forces of information, matter, and energy into transport and conversion within a structure that leads toward the goal. The key lies in continuing the process of refining awareness and information, which may even lead to refining or redefining the Goal itself.

The closed loop systems are called "intelligent" because the process of self-adjustment and refinement is continually going on. In Siddha's understanding of health and disease, for example, the experience of illness – from onset to recovery – is described as a succession of stages. The first stage is awareness; the sense that something is not quite right with your body by using one's Indriyas (senses). At this first stage, even though no detectable symptoms are present, a mindful individual can begin to take corrective action. In terms of systems theory, that action would be an expression of an intelligent system.

Whether it's modern systems theory, which emerged in the 1930s, or Siddha from over five thousand years ago, the concept of intelligence is the same, though the terminology may have changed. Table 3 provides the comparison across both systems of knowledge. The critical difference between an open system and an intelligent system is that that latter begins with a Goal, a mission,or a Sankalpa.

Modern Systems Theory	Siddha
Goal (or Intention)	Sankalpa or Dharma
Disturbances	Vikaras
Sensor	Indriyas
Controller	Manas
Input	Karma
Output	Karma-Phal
Transport	Vata
Conversion	Pitta
Structure (or Storage)	Kapha

Table 3 – Modern systems theory and Siddha.

The discovery of a correlation between modern systems theory and Siddha resulted from my scientific research and study during my Fulbright Fellowship, when I returned to India following my PhD work at MIT. This discovery was published in an eminent engineering systems journal --*The International Journal of Systems of Systems Engineering*-- with the title "The Control Systems Engineering Foundation of Traditional Indian Medicine: The Rosetta Stone for Siddha and Ayurveda."

Anyone interested in reading the original paper can find it online.

CHAPTER 4

Intelligence in Your Home

To make the concept of intelligent systems more real and practical, let's consider a home's central heating system that includes a thermostat. It's a good example of how an intelligent system works. Unlike the open system heater we discussed earlier, this "intelligent" system provides for constant refinement and adjustment of the Input to achieve an Output that matches a specific Goal.

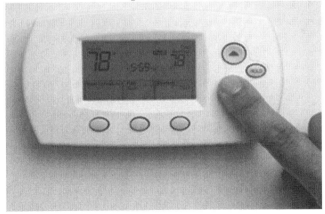

Let's first identify the nine components of the intelligent system using the home heating system.

Goal: If the desired temperature for the apartment is 78 degrees, that's the Goal. It is achieved when the apartment's actual temperature (the Output) and the selected Goal are equal.

Disturbances: The opposite of a Goal, or the opposition to it, are Disturbances. In the thermostat example, the disturbances could be *a cold draft* from an open window in another room. Resolving Disturbances is the key to achieving the Goal. And, this requires accurate and refined Sensors as well as an effective Controller.

Sensor: The sensor is something that can measure the actual temperature in the room – *a thermometer* – within the thermostat. The Sensor communicates the actual real room temperature (the Output) to the Controller. One thing to be aware of is that the sensitivity of the Sensor --- how refined it is in measuring the actual room temperature -- will be critical in achieving the goal of 75 degrees. For example if the thermometer can only measure in 10 degree increments --- temperatures of 60, 70, 80, 90--- then we will never get to 78. At best, we will alternate between 70 and 80. However, if the thermometer can measure in one degree increments, we have a better shot at getting to exactly 78 degrees.

340

Controller: The Controller is the component of the thermostat that receives two pieces of information: 1) what the Goal is --- in this case 75 degrees; and, 2) the actual room temperature from thermometer, which is the sensor. The Controller takes these two pieces of information and determines the difference between the Goal temperature and the Output (or current) temperature. The Controller then sends a new Input into the open system to affect the forces of Transport, Conversion and Structure (or Storage) to produce a new Output.

Transport: The forces of Transport in this case are the flow of heating oil into the furnace. If our current temperature --- the Output --- is too low, say only 60 degrees, then the Input will be to increase the Transport (or flow) of heating oil into the furnace. More heating oil, more heat. If this happens and the heat goes too high -- say to 80 degrees -- the Controller will send an Input to shut off the flow of heating oil into the furnace. In this case, the actual room temperature --- the Output --- will start to drop. In this manner, the flow of heating oil will be increased or stopped by the Controller until the Output matches the Goal.

Conversion: Conversion in this case occurs in the furnace. The furnace takes in the heating oil (matter) and converts it into heat (thermal energy). The more oil, the more heat is produced. Less oil, less heat is produced. No oil, no heat is produced. That simple. This is why you may hear your furnace going on and off on a winter's night as the Controller is either sending in more oil or turning off the oil flow.

Structure: The Structure is composed of the walls, the floors, the insulation, the beams, and the ceiling. These elements form the structure of the house, which provides a container where the forces of Transport and Conversion come together. Clearly, if you have a very well insulated home, then the place will need much less oil to heat, and we can achieve, and more importantly, *maintain* the Goal --- with far less fluctuations. If the home has lots of drafts and poor insulation, heat will escape and the Controller will constantly have to turn on and turn off the flow of oil into the furnace.

Output: The Output is the actual temperature of the room at any point.

In summary, let's consider the following scenario:

A. We set a Goal – 78 degrees.

B. Disturbances such as an open window exist.

C. The Sensor --- the thermometer measures, say, for example, a room temperature of 70 degrees (the Output).

D. The Controller --- let's say, finds the room is 8 degrees in temperature between the desired Goal (78 degrees) and the Output (70 degrees), and makes a decision to increase the Input.

E. The Input increases the Transport to "transport" more oil into the furnace, which performs Conversion to raise the Output (room temperature) to say, for example, 80 degrees.

342

F. The Controller --- for example, may now find the room is now 2 degrees HIGHER in temperature between the Goal (78 degrees) and the Output (80 degrees).

G. The Input is to turn off the flow, Transport, of oil into the furnace, and based on how well the room is insulated or not, the temperature will drop until it reaches the Goal of 78 degrees. At this point, our Goal is achieved.

H. If the Output continues to drop, to say 77 degrees, one degree below our Goal, then the process repeats and we increase the Input to send more oil into the furnace, and the process iterates.

The key feature of intelligent systems is that they are always in flux. They are constantly making adjustments. They are sensing, controlling and modulating the input into the open system. "Perfection" is not the objective, but is only an imaginary concept, which is always being approached but is never permanently sustained.

How does this translate into life in the everyday world? What does it mean to set and achieve goals within the context of an intelligent, feedback system?

The answers to these questions lead to some of the most important concepts in this book. Understanding the relationship between closed loop intelligent systems and goal achievement means embracing the notion of flexibility – certainly in your path toward achieving a goal, and possibly even in the nature of the goal itself.

When I say that a systems approach can enable you to attain any goal you want, that statement includes the possibility that the goal you want at the outset may not be the goal you really want as you move forward.

Here's one of my favorite goal setting stories. Shaquille O'Neal, the basketball player who won several championships with the Los Angeles Lakers, was doing a television interview. The interviewer asked him, "How did you get interested in basketball?"

Shaq laughed. He said, "Well, one day I noticed that I was seven feet tall...."

In other words, he was tall, so it made sense for him to focus on basketball --- to set that as his goal. That doesn't mean he was comfortable with it from the beginning. It doesn't mean it was easy for him. There's nothing more painfully obvious than a really tall guy on the basketball court who isn't any good at the game. Shaq must have gone through a period like that.

But he persisted. Eventually his natural gifts overcame his beginner's deficits. He was physically and mentally gifted to play basketball, and his chosen goal was in sync with his gifts. There were sure to be necessary adjustments along the way, and Shaq integrated them as part of a feedback system designed to take him to his goal. I'm sure he was aware of the gold at the end of the rainbow. If he could master the game of basketball, he would be rich and famous. So he did, and achieved his goal -- what he was cut out to do. This was his *dharma* or his *sankalpa* --- his mission in life.

But suppose that Shaquille O'Neal had wanted to be an opera singer. And suppose he did not have a beautiful

344

or a powerful voice. Can systems theory – or any other approach – legitimately say that he could be an opera singer anyway? Or a brain surgeon? Or a jockey?

No, of course not. But what you will get from systems theory, and especially from the concept of a feedback loop, is an ongoing Input stream that will enable you to make continuous adjustments, and – as you acquire further information – perhaps to reset your priorities.

Before we go forward into looking at some other more interesting and complex examples of systems theory, we are going to visit another simple example to contrast an open system with an intelligent system, so that you really understand the basics of systems theory.

CHAPTER 5

Systems Theory in the Kitchen

The best way to understand systems theory is to look at systems in action. A good everyday example could be making a bowl of soup. But there are two ways of looking at that example. First, we can imagine making soup as an Open system process.

The Open System of Making Soup

It's very simple. Open a can of soup, put the soup in a pan, and turn on the stove for five minutes.

Right now, can you identify the five elements of input, transport, conversion, structure, and output in this open system?

There are three Inputs: (1) opening the can of soup; (2) putting the soup in the bowl; and, (3) turning on the stove for five minutes. The heat activates energies of Conversion to cook the soup. The bowl provides the Structure (and Storage for all the ingredients). The Transport is the flow of heat energy through the bowl and into the soup. After five minutes the Output is heated soup, which is ready to be consumed.

The Intelligent System of Making Soup

But suppose you were a more ambitious chef who wanted to make a large amount of soup using an intelligent system. What are the elements relative to the intelligent system of making soup?

Let's start with the Goal. We don't want just any bowl of soup. We want *a tasty, warm bowl of soup* --- this is our Goal. So far, so good.

But with any Goal, Disturbances will arise. There might be a power outage or an overflow of water. The kitchen might run out of a key ingredient. An important employee might suddenly quit in a huff. If something can go wrong, it often will. These are the potential Disturbances.

Remember, we achieve our Goal by overcoming Disturbances through the use of our Sensors and a Controller.

In this case, our five senses are the Sensors. We can observe how the soup is coming along by watching it. We can use our ears to hear if it boiling too much? Does something smell like its burning? We can taste it so see if it has enough salt, or if it's too spicy or needs more sour taste. We can stir it and feel it with our hands to see if it's too thick or coarse. Our senses are fed back to our Controller.

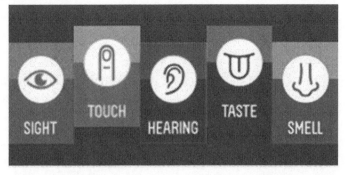

The Controller is you, which includes your experience, your intelligence, and your skill as a chef. Are you getting closer to that tasty, warm bowl of soup? Based on this, you decide what action and inputs you are going to take and keep adjusting the inputs, until you achieve our Goal.

The Inputs could include adding or removal of ingredients, choosing to cover the pan, adding more salt, and increasing the flame.

Transport is the movement of heat and mechanical forces inside the bowl, including the simple motion of moving heat as we stir the ingredients.

Next comes the energy of Conversion. The fire that heats the soup embodies this energy.

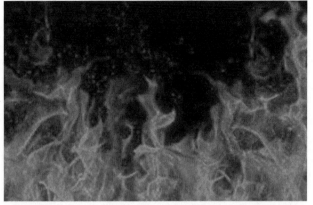

The Structure is provided by the vessel, which the ingredients are cooked and stirred.

The Goal is reached when, after continuously sensing the soup (tasting it, smelling it, touching it) and making adjustments with our Goal in mind, we get an Output, which are tasty bowls of homemade soup!

Here's a point-by-point review of the steps we've covered from a systems perspective:

>> **Goal**: Tasty and warm bowl of soup.

>> **Disturbance**: This refers to any distractions or interruptions in the soup-making process.

>> **Sensors**: These are the chef's senses and perceptions. Is the soup getting too hot? Is the fire too high or too low? Are any spices or other ingredients needed?

>> **Controller**: An intelligent and attentive chef is an effective Controller. In this context, intelligent doesn't mean high IQ. It's the chef's experience and common sense.

>> **Input**: Ingredients of the soup. These are the raw materials on which the intelligent system is based.

>> Transport: The heating and stirring of the ingredients. This is the "action" element of the system. It's movement and adjustment. Too much or too little can complicate the process and affect the output.

>> Conversion: The fire that heats the soup. Like the ingredients of the soup, this is "raw" material. The correct application of the fire depends on the controller, the transport, and the sensors.

>> Structure: The container in which the ingredients are heated. The nature of the container – is it a pan or much larger cauldron? -- can influence all aspects of the system.

>> Output: The state of the bowl of soup at any point in time during the preparation process. At some point, it may be too salty, not enough vegetables, not hot enough, etc. Remember, the mission here is to get an Output that matches the desired Goal.

In all areas of our lives – in the kitchen and everywhere else -- we have goals and disturbances, and we also have systems theory to help us resolve the opposition between those two elements.

And we have choice. We can choose to be open systems --- such as simply opening that can of soup and heating it, without much intelligence, or we can set our own goals, as in the case of being a goal-oriented chef to get what we want.

One can argue that most human beings may be open systems --- simply taking in inputs, reacting to them, and producing an output. Open systems do not have a goal, they do not seek to achieve a goal, nor do they "work" towards a goal. They simply react to the input.

And once again, there's nothing wrong with that provided it's what you really want. In the next Part that follows, we'll look at the process of how the nine elements of intelligent systems operate in the life journeys of characters in grand epics to compelling dramas to understand how one can achieve goals in the face of disturbances.

PART 2

The 7 Step Systems Program

CHAPTER 6

The Systems Approach to Life

Now, let's put theory into practice to solve some real problems. Perhaps the three most important and immediate problems that affect many people in the modern world are: health, wealth and love.

Systems theory provides a practical way to approach and find real solutions to such problems. In the subsequent chapters, I am going to teach you, in a step-by-step, systematic manner, how to solve such problems. These examples will give you the confidence to tackle any problem in life.

Remember, problems in life can be approached as an open system or as an intelligent system. If you truly want to achieve goals in life, you need to take an intelligent systems approach. You may be tempted to take an open systems approach, and you can make that choice. But remember that if you choose an open system, you may be "outsourcing" your decision-making to someone else, and you will forfeit your power to take on life's challenges -- life's disturbances --- on your own.

STEP 1: SEE, FEEL, HEAR, SMELL, AND TASTE THE GOAL

To reach any goal, you must first set that Goal and bring it into your consciousness clearly and specifically. That means connecting with the goal in your thoughts, your emotions, and with all your senses. Use your imagination. Challenge yourself to see, feel, hear, smell, and perhaps, even taste, the Goal. Make the goal real in your mind, and you'll be well on the way to making it real in the physical world.

Consider this real world example: Lynn is a recent college graduate with a degree in anthropology. She is looking forward to entering the business world in order to make new friends, earn a good salary, and pay off her student loans.

Her high level goal may be to get a job in human resources that will allow her to use her knowledge of cultural diversity in a corporate setting. But this is not yet very tangible until she can literally see it, taste it, feel it, etc.

In this case, a more powerful goal description would be:

"I want to get 3 job offers in human resources, within the next 60-days for a job that is located in Santa Monica with nearby great restaurants, working with amazing people from all over the world in a professional environment with core values similar to mine, and close to my gym so I can stay in shape."

This goal has clarity. It has a deadline: 60-days. Stating it as such, provides a way for Lynn to visualize it clearly.

STEP 2: IDENTIFY THE DISTURBANCES

What are the obstacles -- both internal and external -- that stand between you and your goal? It's important to be very clear about this, so make a list. Here are the disturbances that Lynn identified:

- She felt she had good academic training but was unfamiliar with the business world
- She was somewhat shy and was reluctant to present herself in person as proactively as she should
- She tended to get depressed when a lead did not pan out

STEP 3: IDENTIFY WHICH INTELLIGENT SYSTEM FORCES -- TRANSPORT, CONVERSION, OR STRUCTURE -- WILL BE MOST HELPFUL IN OVERCOMING THE DISTURBANCES?

One, two, or all three of the forces of Transport, Conversion or Structure can be used to offset the disturbance.

This step is crucial to "being intelligent." Here, Lynn must identify, which of the three or all or some need to be used to combat that disturbance, to offset the disturbance.

Lynn decided that Transport and Structure were most important for her. Transport would help her to be more energetic and outgoing. Structure would keep her focused and organized.

STEP 4: WHICH INPUTS CAN SUPPORT THE FORCES YOU'VE CHOSEN?

What are things you can actually input into yourself or into your environment that will activate, express, and support the forces you've chosen?

For the forces of Transport and Structure, here are Lynn's Inputs:

- **For Transport** -- she would start moving, taking action: visit her university's post-grad employment office three times a week....she would redesign her resume and include a new photograph....she would join a running club and train for an upcoming 10k event to meet others, and get herself literally moving to overcome her lethargy and shyness. These activities would be to get her resume and her skills known and circulated among as many relevant people as possible

- **For Structure** -- each evening she would make a to-do list for the next day....she would give herself structure by formalizing a schedule on when to go to bed and wake up at a reasonable hour....she would set aside time to see friends and socialize on weekends.

STEP 5: WHAT OUTPUTS CAN MEASURE YOUR PROGRESS?

The inputs into the system will lead to outputs. But one needs to be able to identify the specific outputs that are a tangible measure of progress towards the goal. In Lynn's case, the outputs would be:

- The number of new contacts she made each day
- How many interviews she was called in for
- How many job offers she received

STEP 6: IDENTIFY THE SENSORS (THE TOOLS) YOU WILL NEED TO MEASURE THE OUTPUTS

Sensors are tangible tools that one uses to measure outputs. For example, in the thermostat example, the sensor is the thermometer that is needed to measure the output of temperature.

In this case, Lynn can use spreadsheet technology as a measurement tool that tracks the Output, as follows:

	Contacts	Interviews	Offers
Day 1			
Day 2			
...			
Day 60			

This is her Sensor. It provides tangible measure of her outputs. The Sensor allows Lynn to literally see her progress day to day.

STEP 7: ACTIVATE YOUR CONTROLLER

The Controller in systems theory is the "brain" that first objectively looks at the reality results (the Outputs) that stem from actions (the Inputs).

For example, the Sensor may reveal to Lynn that by day 45 -- while she got 100 contacts -- she only got one interview and not a single job offer. This is clearly not good. She had better make some decisions to drive new Inputs into her system; otherwise, she can forget ever coming close to her goal.

What can this mean? Perhaps out of those 100 contacts she is not spending quality time with most of them and deepening her relationships with them, so that they support her in getting interviews. In that case, her new Input will be to review those contacts and identify a few influencers, contact them and perhaps set aside lunch meetings, and update her resume.

These changes would most likely involve adjustments to her Inputs, but they could also include a basic reconsideration of her goal of joining the corporate world.

BRINGING IT ALL TOGETHER

The seven steps we've covered in this chapter represent a systematic path toward achieving your chosen goal from a systems-based approach. Together, they're a way of making progress, but their purpose is not for achieving perfection --- which is an illusion. The key is commitment to make the necessary course corrections. Such adjustments and corrections will always be necessary and should even be welcomed.

That's why Step 7 is so important.

In Step 7 your Controller considers where you are and where you're going, and gives you the freedom to take a fresh look at everything. Taken together, these steps should be challenging but not overwhelming. Follow them and there's a good chance you'll get what you want, and you'll definitely get what you need.

CHAPTER 7

Your System, Your Weight

According to the National Institutes of Health, more than a third of Americans meet the clinical definition of obesity and approximately 70 percent of the population is at least somewhat overweight.

That's bad news for lots of people but it's good news for authors and publishers of "magic-bullet" diet books. Those books are a billion dollar business. What's more, you can almost certainly find a diet book that will give you permission to keep eating exactly what you've been eating all along, with the promise that you can lose weight while doing it.

High protein diets, for example, have emphasized lean meats, fish, eggs, and beans. But what if you wanted to eat carbs and fats? Well, that's fine. A recent volume by best selling author advocates a high fat diet. But that doesn't take people's individual chemistry into account.

There may be some people for whom a high fat diet will work. There may be many more who aren't at all suited for a high fat diet. But they'll only find that out after they've spent their money on the book.

The Open Systems Approach to Losing Weight

Without delving into the specifics of fad diets, I have a problem with them from a systems theory perspective. They're one-dimensional and reductionist. They're open systems in the sense that your own intelligence plays no part. You're just following the rote directions of a diet guru and hoping for the best that things will work out.

You just buy the book, and buy whatever foods the guru tells you to buy, and eat that food.

However, sooner or later, an open system diet will fail. For one thing, open system diets assume a level of lifestyle predictability that doesn't exist in the real world. In systems terminology, that unpredictability expresses itself as disturbances. A raw food diet might sound very pure and authentic, but what happens if some of your raw food harbors a virulent parasite -- which could be quite likely if you were sent on business to India or China? A high protein diet could be difficult to sustain if you're in an area where high quality meat and seafood isn't available.

The rigidity of open system diets brings up many such problems. If you're an Inuit fisherman living in Alaska, convincing you to eat a raw food diet makes no sense. Neither does it make sense to attempt a high fat diet if you're living in the desert. Trying to follow a program that is incongruent with individual circumstances only creates stress, which then becomes a problem in itself. Inevitably, you will become

364

demoralized and drop out of the diet. Good health comes from understanding your environment, and also adjusting to changes in that environment. That requires an intelligent systems approach.

The Intelligent Systems Approach to Losing Weight

So let's look at losing weight as an intelligent system. Let's approach the issue as fully functioning human beings who are intelligent, rather than as robots. Here's how that looks, step by step:

STEP 1: SET A GOAL

Let's assume you want to lose 20 pounds. Millions of people, perhaps even the majority of Americans, would benefit from doing just that. The more specific your goal is, the more efficient your weight loss system will be.

So let's get it more visual and clear by stating that you want to:

- Lose 20 pounds;
- Feel great when you look at yourself; and,
- Be lean and healthy

This statement of goals makes it a bit more real and tangible.

STEP 2: IDENTIFY DISTURBANCES

As we've seen, open system methods to losing weight ignore disturbances, but an intelligent system deals with them right away. Remember, your goal is to lose weight in a manner that is sustainable. If you're not able to manage disturbances along the way, you're going to fail.

What are the present or potential issues standing between you and your goal of losing twenty pounds, feeling great, and looking lean and healthy? Let's itemize those disturbances.

- Time constraints: You're pressed for time by work or other responsibilities, and the diet is no longer a top priority
- Location constraints: You travel and your schedule makes it hard to get the foods you need
- Motivational issues: Will you lose motivation if you don't see immediate results?
- Unsupportive environment: Can you continue to follow your plan even when others around you aren't supportive?

STEP 3: IDENTIFY WHICH INTELLIGENT SYSTEM FORCES -- TRANSPORT, CONVERSION, OR STRUCTURE -- WILL BE MOST HELPFUL IN OVERCOMING THE DISTURBANCES?

For losing weight, you will need to invoke all three forces.

Transport. In systems theory, transport refers to the presence of motion within a system. Transport is a key element of weight loss. It includes not only the motion that comes with full-body exercise, but also the motion of food through your digestive system.

Conversion. The bottom line of any diet is the ability of your body to efficiently convert the input of food into an output of energy rather than excess weight.

366

Optimal conversion also means you can eat less food and get more energy.

Structure. Structure and Strength of your physical, mental, and spiritual being will be essential for weight loss and control. If you're not mentally strong, you won't have the discipline to follow any diet. If you're not physically strong, you won't be able exercise.

STEP 4: WHICH INPUTS CAN SUPPORT THE FORCES YOU'VE CHOSEN?

Each of the three forces responds positively to specific Inputs.

For example, there are several actions you can take to optimize Transport:

- Physically move - exercise, walk, etc. There are so many choices these days. The key is to find something you enjoy and move the body for at least 15-30 minutes per day.
- Eat more fiber and roughage, such as nuts and seeds. Today, in modern times, we eat a fraction of the fiber our ancestors ate. Increased fiber will support the movement of food and waste through our digestive system.
- Make raw foods and salads a part of your diet every day. Raw foods provide motion, and are great for the summer times in particular.

Conversion is activated by performing those activities that optimize digestion. Such activation can involve how you prepare food, how you eat your food, what supplements you use.

To increase Conversion:

- Include digestive enzymes in your diet. Your consumption of digestive enzymes is essential, since they are usually absent from an everyday diet. Enzymes are the drivers of nearly every chemical reaction in our bodies. Fast food, and most restaurant foods and processed foods can be enlivened and made more digestible by adding in digestive enzymes. If you have a sluggish digestive system, enzymes are like a high performance fuel that energize and clean out the system.

- Use spices to energize your metabolism. Spices and in particular curries which include a combination of spices such as cumin, ginger, turmeric are highly beneficial. Siddha teaches that these spices increase metabolism by activating the principle of pitta --- the force of Conversion.

- The incorporation of ketogenic or "high fat," using the right fats, diets are really aimed at supporting the burning (conversion) of fats tools such as the "Bulletproof Coffee" and others aim to support the conversion element of your system.

- Follow the rules of good food combining. Food combining is the art of eating. What you eat first, what you eat last, what you eat things with, are key to digestion. You can look up food combining charts online that will provide you the details. The basics are proteins that combine well with fats and leafy greens. Carbs and proteins should be avoided together (or take enzymes if you are going to combine them).

- Slow cooking. Slow cooking is an amazing way to pre-digest foods. Slow cooking breaks down foods so you can absorb more nutrients. There are great slow cooking books.
- Fermented foods. These foods support your gut bacteria --- your microbiome ---- so you have an optimal environment in your gut for digestion and absorption and general wellbeing.
- Take probiotic supplements. Like fermented foods, they support your microbiome.
- Eat clean foods whenever possible such as organic and non-GMO foods. A powerful engine is one that is a clean engine. Clean foods support a clean engine.

Structure benefits from a good exercise program, which should include a combination of building strength through resistance, as in weight training, and building flexibility through yoga or other stretching practice. In order to stay motivated, try to do this together with other people who also want to lose weight and be healthy.

These are the Inputs that will positively affect your Structure:

Strength training

- Concentration and mindfulness: be still for 15 minutes and observe your breath. This is a meditation called *Vipasana*, which means "seeing things as they really are." Such practices help to modulate cortisol levels and thereby support weight loss.

- Eat a moderate amount of fats, which have a calming effect by modulating the firing of your nerves, and help to burn fat. Yes, eating fat doesn't mean you put on fat, in fact, you will burn fat and lose weight.
- Eat the right kinds of proteins for your body type. Your Body, Your System tool can help you identify these in Part III. Protein provides amino acids, the foundation structural element of muscles.
- Sleep is critical to losing weight. Those who do not sleep well have high cortisol, which leads to fat storage (too much structure).
- Portion control is another important aspect of weight management, and this a part of managing *how much* "material" or food you input into your Structure. Programs like Weight Watchers primarily focus on this aspect.

STEP 5: WHAT OUTPUTS CAN MEASURE YOUR PROGRESS?

There are many outputs you can measure. For our specific goals, here are three outputs that you can measure that will provide you an indication if you are on the right path to weight loss each day:

- Your actual weight
- The size of your waist and arms
- How you look in the mirror and feel about yourself

STEP 6: IDENTIFY THE SENSORS YOU NEED TO MEASURE THE OUTPUTS

Three important tools will act as your weight loss sensors:

- a scale
- a measuring tape
- a camera

Use these sensors to determine where you are at the outset of your weight loss program, and use them again at regular intervals to determine the output of the program. It's important to be mindful of the process, and objective measures are an essential means for implementing that.

It's easy to create a simple grid for keeping track of the changing information from your sensors. That information is the output of your weight loss system.

	Week 1	Week 2	Week 3	Week 4
Scale (Your weight in lbs. or kg)				
Tape measure (Waist size and arm size)				
Camera (pictures of yourself)				

STEP 7: ACTIVATE YOUR CONTROLLER.

Based on the tracking of your output -- your weight, your measurements, and your pictures -- your Controller should make a rational assessment of how far you are from your goal. Simply put, you as the Controller should measure the differential between where you are now and where you intend to be.

You can use a use a measurement from 1 to 10 to clearly express how far you are from your Goal relative to each output. If you want to lose 20 pounds and you've lost 10, then right now you're at point 5, or 50 percent, with 5 more points to go. Take photos of yourself at weekly intervals in a more qualitative measure. But you can still express your progress on the 1-10 scale.

BRINGING IT ALL TOGETHER

Implementing an intelligent system for weight loss should always include mindful awareness of how well the system is moving toward your goal, and adjusting the system accordingly. See things as they really are -- and remember that you are engaged in an iterative experience in which the ongoing objective is participation and progress, not perfection. This isn't about following the latest fad diet from some celebrity. Those programs aren't really about you losing weight. Unfortunately, they're about making someone else rich.

As we've discussed, open system diets are one-dimensional in their emphasis on one food category or a single activity. Raw food, for example, is useful for increasing transport, but it won't help if you need more fats to increase Structure. Or if you're leading a sedentary lifestyle, you can benefit from daily exercise, and spices in your diet to facilitate Transport and Conversion.

Above all, remember that your body belongs to you. Be the captain of your own fate. Be the artist of who you are. Diet gurus care about taking money out of your pocket. Whatever you put into your mouth, and whatever you bring into your life, is and should be your choice alone.

CHAPTER 8

Your System, Your Wealth

If you visit the Smithsonian Museum in Washington DC, you'll see that an entire division of the institution is devoted to innovation. Specifically, you can see row upon row of glass cases containing models of tools and other products that were created by ordinary Americans in the 19th and early 20th centuries. The models were submitted to the government as part of the innovator's' patent applications.

It's impressive to see how people all over the country were coming up with labor-saving ideas that they hoped would also be money-making. Sometimes they were right and sometimes they were wrong. But they all believed that innovation was worth their time and effort.

It was only relatively recently, in the mid-20th century, during and post WWII that Americans turned away from innovation and entrepreneurship. Instead, we began to depend on long-term corporate or manufacturing employment as a way to secure our

374

future. Union wages and retirement pensions became a way of life. Fifty years earlier most people had lived on farms, but now the suburbs were becoming the dominant population centers.

Work was done sitting down. So was leisure. Financial stability, or even affluence, was understood as an open system. Get a job with a corporation, stay with it, and then retire.

The Open Systems Approach to Wealth

In the midst of this change, many are still seeking enormous wealth wherever they think it can be found. In this effort, many are tempted by an open systems approach to making wealth. Extremes of this approach include: buy lottery tickets, hitting the poker tables at Vegas, or getting the latest stock tip at the water cooler.

Other variations of this include getting a person to whom you outsource responsibility for your financial wellbeing: a wealth guru, financial planner or money manager. In such cases, you give them your money, you wait 3-6 months, and hope for the best. If they lose your money, they blame it on the "market disturbances."

If you can resist the illusion of open systems, please read on. After starting seven companies, I've learned quite a bit about wealth building through innovation.

The Intelligent Systems Approach to Create Wealth

Real wealth for yourself and others around you comes from recapturing the spirit and skill of innovation that used to define us. We've got to go back to the future. We've got to build wealth the old fashioned way.

The stories of Indian gods and goddesses, which I heard again and again as a child, teach that success follows innovation. Lakshmi the goddess of wealth follows Shiva, the god of creation.

Innovation is once again the key to wealth. Our wealth creation, in this chapter, will focus on building a profitable business through the authentic creativity and innovation of an intelligent system approach to starting a new business.

Fortunately, innovation is in everyone's DNA. You can start your own venture wherever you are, even if it's only online. You don't have to be in Silicon Valley. Every company, even Google and Microsoft, started small, and at that stage every decision can magnify into a long-lasting effect.

STEP 1: SET A GOAL

In the environment of a startup company, things are always changing very quickly. In this case, for illustrative purposes, we are going to assume that the startup is a business-to-business service company that also uses its online presence to generate leads. With that in mind, it's best to set flexible goals within a well-defined and relatively short time frame, because if your business doesn't have positive trajectory short-term, it's likely not going to succeed long-term.

I have found six months is a practical time frame for goal setting. Here are three essential questions to setting your specific goals: What do you want to achieve in the next six months? Do you have enough cash to make those achievements possible? How many new customers can you acquire during that period? Can you develop a powerful pipeline?

Below are the specific goals that I have found are relevant in most early stage startups. These goals are based on a six month time line:

- Enough cash (i.e. $500,000)
- Acquire new customers (i.e. 5)
- Excellent customer service (i.e. defined by 80% of customer base delighted with the service.)

Acquiring new customers is vitally important because you will learn from them. Five new, high quality customers in a six month period is a reasonable goal. Through those customers, you'll learn what you're doing well and what you need to improve. You'll learn how to deliver your product on time. You'll gain experience in dealing with special requests and different kinds of people.

You'll also make some mistakes, and you'll recover from them. And meanwhile, make sure you don't run out of cash. If you're setting goals for a six month time frame, you should have enough cash for the next eighteen months.

STEP 2: IDENTIFY DISTURBANCES.

For a new company, problems with customer service are the primary cause of disturbances. This usually takes the form of over-promising and not delivering. In your eagerness to acquire new customers, it's easy to tell them what you think they want to hear instead of what you can actually do.

Common disturbances in early stage startups include:

- Poor customer service
- Inability to close sales
- Missing deadlines and delivery dates

Your customer service employees need high motivation to contact new clients and close deals, but they also need to be realistic about what those clients should expect. Your project managers should not over-promise, but they had better deliver on time. Your salespeople are only as good as their ability to convert leads into closed sales.

STEP 3: IDENTIFY WHICH INTELLIGENT SYSTEM FORCES -- TRANSPORT, CONVERSION, OR STRUCTURE -- WILL BE MOST HELPFUL IN OVERCOMING THE DISTURBANCES?

For a startup business or a new company, all three forces are essential:

Transport. In any startup business, the principle of transport is embodied by creative employees. These are the designers, the engineers, the marketers who create content for your websites. They are the ones who really inspire and move your customers to use your products. They create the websites, the ad campaigns, and the look and feel of your products. You would not be "moved" to buy the iPhone if it didn't look as good as it does. Creative talent can literally make your customers jump to buy your product.

Conversion. Sales personnel are the basic expression of Conversion in a new company. Money has to be brought in -- otherwise you will run out of cash or be forced to find an investor who will take a big chunk of your company, losing the control and freedom that first inspired you to start your business. Deals need to be closed. It can't be just a matter of talking or planning or "strategy." Customers need to sign on the dotted line. Leads need to be converted to actual sales, delivering cash into the bank!

Structure. The principle of structure in a startup company is personified by the administrators, accountants, attorneys, secretaries, receptionists, and even the custodial staff, as well as the physical structure in which the forces of Transport and Conversion can take place. This includes the company WiFi, the internet connection, the computers, the laptops and the physical building in which you house your employees. The ability of this structure to be fast, nimble and flexible will determine your success. A stodgy lawyer who takes months to review a contract could mean a lost prospective customer. An IT department that can't keep the servers running will mean poor customer service.

STEP 4: WHICH INPUTS CAN SUPPORT THE FORCES YOU'VE CHOSEN?

For each of the forces that we've identified, we need the right Inputs to achieve our goal.

To optimize the power of Transport, the Input of hiring the right creative and engineering staff who can

379

work together as a team for creating compelling products is critical.

There can't be any ego issues, no prima donnas. Creative personnel may naturally be heavily invested in a particular idea of their own --- but this is not arts school or design theory. If clients aren't responding there's no time for hard feelings. Changes have to be made fast, and the team may have to brainstorm quickly to changing market conditions.

A quick aside I learned, for example, that hiring people, even for seemingly minor positions, needed to be done very carefully, and sometimes you have to make tough choices on the spectrum of competence versus integrity. Sometimes it was tempting to take on someone who had a track record of sales, but whose ethics were questionable. I learned, however, that one individual with lack of integrity, no matter how competent, can destroy a fledgling startup of 5 or 10 team members.

This is the kind of fundamental principle that needs to be understood when you're getting a business off the ground. When I taught a class on entrepreneurship at MIT, I was surprised by the number of students who were confused about how to decide this specific issue. Yet it's a decision that can make or break a new company.

To optimize Conversion, the important Input is to ensure leads are converted to closed sales from leads. This means you need sales personnel who are "Closers" and techniques that support conversion (e.g. good marketing material, excellent presentations, analysis of the competition, and clear messaging on why your product is better.)

A huge pipeline of leads is useless without someone who can convert them to cash flow. Despite what you may have heard, talk is not cheap. Lots of talk and no closing is not a system for building wealth.

I remember one of my mentors sharing a great story about two sales people who had very different personalities. One didn't like to travel and made cold calls all day doing presentations on the phone. The other loved to take trips to meet customers face to face, and was constantly flying around the country.

One day the traveling salesman returned from a trade show in Las Vegas and boasted to the cold calling sales guy, on all the people he'd met, how many restaurants he'd eaten at, how many hands he shook, and all the great meetings he had. It had been a great adventure.

So, the cold calling sales guy, sitting at his desk, looked up and asked "So I guess you didn't close any sales either."

It doesn't matter if you cold-call or spend money talking in five star restaurants --- no conversion means no sales.

To optimize Structure, the Input you need involves implementing processes, protocols, and procedures across the Company to ensure that your systems work 24x7 with 99.99% uptime of your computers and your network.

Delivery has to occur on time. To do this you need detail-oriented personnel who are table, flexible and highly competent. Your accounting books need to be accurate, and you'd better follow the relevant laws and corporate governance so you don't get shut down.

It's not glamorous stuff, but it's important. Along the same lines, create a physical setting that encourages innovative thinking and positive energy. Silicon Valley is famous for this, with many company headquarters that look more like Legoland than billion dollar firms.

STEP 5: WHAT OUTPUTS CAN MEASURE YOUR PROGRESS?

The above inputs will lead to Outputs, and you better be able to measure them clearly. To achieve the above goals, those Outputs include:

- Amount of cash in the bank
- Customer satisfaction levels
- How many new customers are signing up?

STEP 6: IDENTIFY THE SENSORS YOU NEED TO MEASURE THE OUTPUTS

Sensors again are the tangible tools that one uses to measure outputs. For the three outputs identified above, here are the sensors you will need:

1. Weekly and monthly cash flow reports - How much revenue is coming in and how much is going out?
2. Weekly and monthly customer service reports - What is the current status of your work for each of your clients? For each client, how would your customer satisfaction rate on a 1-10 scale?
3. Sales "pipeline" reports - These reports should include the following elements:

- Number of leads
- Number of meetings in negotiation
- Signed contracts

STEP 7: ACTIVATE YOUR CONTROLLER

Based on information from your sensors and outputs, the controller will measure the difference between your present status and the achievement of your goals.

For example, assume your goal is having at least $40,000 per month to run your business. But suppose you are in your the third month of operation and have burned through $450,000 of your initial $500,000. You're in serious trouble. You will only have $50,000 left in the bank. You're going to have to shut down your company or you better Input into your system new methods to rapidly close sales.

If your customer service report shows 80% of your customers are angry and all rate LOW versus HIGH or GOOD, you are also in serious trouble. Because LOW customer satisfaction means, you are not going to get referrals or references for new customers. So, better Input more Transport into your system by implementing a new hiring process of getting better customer service employees or fix the bugs in your product, and address problems fast. Personnel may need to be evaluated and changes may need to be made.

Finally, if there are inadequate prospects in the sales pipeline, new approaches may be needed. A well-established principle of customer acquisition is known as "ten-three-one." In order to close one sale, you will need to negotiate with three prospects, and in order to open a negotiation you will need to have made ten initial leads. If, for example, many contacts are being made but no negotiations are in progress, the controller should develop a strategy for identifying higher quality contacts.

BRINGING IT ALL TOGETHER

The elements we've discussed represent a systems approach to wealth creation through building a business. These elements should be continually serviced and kept up to date through weekly management meetings. Cash flow, customer service, and new business pipeline need ongoing attention. Always feel free to look back and re-evaluate both your Inputs and your Goal.

Remember that business is both an art and a science. It's really about combining all the relevant components. If your customers dislike your product, you will have to increase Transport. Get better designers and better engineers. If your sales team is great at getting leads but can't close deals, this is a Conversion issue. You may need to hire talented closers or identify a different sales approach. If your vendors are upset, and your website is slow, then you'll have to address issues of Structure.

The principles of an intelligent system are separate but also interwoven. Take care of all of them, and they'll take care of you.

CHAPTER 9

Your System, Your Love

In all of human history, there has probably never been as much time, money, and energy devoted to finding a soul mate as is now the case. As with so many other areas of life, the Internet has revolutionized this pursuit. There are dozens of online dating sites, each with its own unique slant.

Of course, there are also still possibilities for meeting the old fashioned ways, in a bar or grocery store. But despite all these possibilities, or because of them, the frustrations and disappointments in finding love are as widespread as ever.

The Open Systems Approach to Finding Love

From a systems perspective, all the high tech dating opportunities are just open systems. Nothing has really changed except the system now exists online instead of in a bar. There's the promise of a silver bullet solution if you just buy into the program. Whether it's pickup lines or dating profiles, what's being offered is dependency on an open system rather than active participating and taking responsibility in an intelligent one.

The Intelligent Systems Approach to Finding Love

The spiritual traditions around the world teach that finding your soulmate is anything but easy. Plato's dialogue on love, entitled the Symposium, includes passages that describe human beings as originally being of only one sex. But the gods, fearing that the unisex version of humanity would be too powerful, then divided the genders. Ever since that primal separation, people have been struggling to regain their original unity by finding their perfectly compatible other half. And for most people, the struggle has been in vain.

Mystical Judaism has a similar perspective. While admitting and even celebrating the concept of soulmates, the ancient rabbis taught that actually finding one's soulmate is a greater miracle that the dividing of the Red Sea in the biblical book of Exodus.

But waiting for a miracle is just an open systems approach. Let's see how an intelligent system can help you find the love of your life.

STEP 1: SET A GOAL

The first step in creating an intelligent system for finding love involves defining an individualized goal. What is it that you really want in another person – whether it's a relationship for a certain length of time, or a certain level of financial security, or a degree of physical attraction? All these are differentiators that define your goal.

Let's assume that your goal is a long term, loving relationship that could ultimately develop into marriage and children.

Very succinctly, your current goals would include meeting someone who is:

- Attractive to you and finds you attractive
- Loyal and committed to the same degree as yourself
- Could become a lifetime partner in marriage and family

STEP 2: IDENTIFY DISTURBANCES

There are many possibilities here. Identifying disturbances means accurately assessing who you are, compared to who you might like to think you are. For these reasons, your sensors are extremely important for identifying issues such as the following:

- You don't have enough time for this commitment.
- You're not in a location where you can realistically expect to meet someone.
- You've not taken sufficient care of yourself – physically or financially -- to make yourself reasonably attractive.

STEP 3: IDENTIFY WHICH INTELLIGENT SYSTEM FORCES -- TRANSPORT, CONVERSION, OR STRUCTURE -- WILL BE

MOST HELPFUL IN OVERCOMING THE DISTURBANCES?

In pursuing this goal, all three forces will be required.

Transport in systems theory always refers to the power of action and movement. This can be taken very literally. It's unlikely the love of your life is going to come knocking on your door.

Conversion in finding a relationship isn't very different from conversion in sales. It's a numbers game. The more people you encounter, provided they're legitimate prospects, the greater your chances of success.

Structure refers to environment. If you want to meet someone with a high level corporate career but you're working long hours at a fast food restaurant, your structural element is not in sync with your aspiration.

STEP 4: WHICH INPUTS CAN SUPPORT THE FORCES YOU'VE CHOSEN?

Input means actually doing something to yourself or to your surroundings to enhance the forces of Transport, Conversion and Structure.

To benefit Transport, you could change jobs or move to a new location for a fresh start. You will have to get out into the world, make yourself accessible, and develop yourself as an attractive man or woman. Get the air around you into motion. Open your mouth and talk. See yourself as another person might see you and commit to meeting his or her legitimate expectations.

To benefit Conversion, you could make a plan to meet a certain number of people each week and eventually those initial meetings into more dates and follow ups, and perhaps even serious discussions about the future. Yes, there may be something called "luck" and "love at first sight" -- but you can create those situations by simply getting out there meeting more people.

To benefit Structure, you need to get your "act together" to meet the demands of a person you want to attract. You could give your house or apartment a thorough cleaning, or you may even repaint it. When was the last time you had your car washed? Or even washed it yourself?

STEP 5: WHAT OUTPUTS CAN MEASURE YOUR PROGRESS?

Ask yourself how it might affect your ability to connect with someone. Will you be able and willing to fully participate in a dating relationship, or will you be dependent on the other person? Do you consider yourself to be physically attractive, or are there things you'd like to change? Further, regardless of your personal qualities, if you're living in an area where meeting people is difficult, there's a good chance it's not going to happen.

If there are deficits in your personal health, your financial situation, or your physical location, the results of those deficits will express themselves in your Outputs.

Rate yourself on a 1-10 scale:

Your Health & Appearance	
Your Financial Situation	
Your Geographical Location	

STEP 6: IDENTIFY THE SENSORS YOU NEED TO MEASURE THE OUTPUTS

You can gain some valuable objectivity by making use of some basic tools:

- A camera -- do you really look the way you think you look?
- Your financial information - is your bank account solvent? Is your income secure?
- Your geographical location -- it may be easier to meet someone in New York rather than Alaska.

STEP 7: ACTIVATE YOUR CONTROLLER

For better or worse, be aware of how you've gotten to where you are. Sometimes habits can seem like inevitabilities. You need to deal with that possibility, which is where your controller comes into play.

Your controller must formulate a strategy to close the gap between your goal in finding a relationship and who you are physically, what you have financially, and where you are geographically. In a word, this is about compatibility.

In terms of the three elements included in the chart in Step 5, how close are you to your goals on the 1-10 scale, and what can you do to close the gap? And when you meet someone, you can assess your compatibility with that person using the same scale. To reach a 10 level in each category, you may need to make some major lifestyle changes. You may also want and expect a prospective partner to do the same.

The "ten-three-one" ratio used in sales also applies to finding a life partner.

You must prospect at least ten people for every three in which you'll find some interest. Out of those three, you should then be able to get at least one worthwhile face-to-face meeting.

Track the number and status of contacts in your "pipeline" and the progress of those connections:

GOOD

Number of contacts	100
First dates	30
Serious possibilities for the future	10

BAD

Number of contacts	50
First dates	10
Serious possibilities for the future	1

BRINGING IT ALL TOGETHER

As the old saying goes, if you keep doing what you've always done then don't expect a different result. Be flexible. In order to meet someone you really care about -- and who will really care about you -- don't rule anything out.

This is an important part of your life, maybe the most important part. Optimize your Transport, Conversion, and Structure, and look for someone who's ready and willing to do the same.

When you're ready to make changes like these, your love life and your life as a whole will change for the better.

PART 3

Your Body, Your System

CHAPTER 10

Your Body's Goal: Natural System State

Your body is an intelligent system. Intelligent systems as we have seen are based on the desire to achieve a Goal. According to the traditional wisdom of Siddha, the body has a natural intelligence and it inherently knows its Goal --- which is known as its *Prakriti* or its *Natural Systems State*. The Natural System State is the unique combination of the forces of Transport, Conversion and Structure inherent in you as an individual, where your body operates at its highest potential and can heal itself.

In Siddha, such a state of health is defined as you achieving the goal of your body's Natural System State. Most of us are not even aware of our body's Natural System State. Disturbances, moreover, get in the way and perturb us away from our Natural System State.

Therefore, in Siddha the pathway to health begins by knowing our Natural System State – the goal, knowing how Disturbances have moved us away from this goal, and then making the adjustments through the inputs of food, exercise and supplements to bring us back to our Natural System State.

To begin: what is your natural systems state? In terms of systems theory, who is it that you really are? The forces of Transport, Conversion, and Structure affect all forms of matter, energy and information throughout nature. The strength of these forces varies from one life form to another. That strength also varies among individuals – including you -- within a given species.

The importance of these variations is being recognized by Western medicine as better diagnostic tools become available and as genome research reveals the individual character of human DNA. But the concept that every person's physiology is a system with an individualized balance of energies has existed for thousands of years. This became clear to me when I received a Fulbright grant that allowed me to return to India for study of the ancient health tradition of Siddha.

The Siddhars – the term means "enlightened ones" -- used their own bodies as experimental laboratories to understand the interaction of three essential forces which they called Vata, Pitta, and Kapha.

As we've seen, it's surprising – or maybe it's not surprising – that the Siddha principles of Vata, Pitta, and Kapha are exact parallels of Transport, Conversion, and Structure. Perhaps systems theory is simply a new terminology for an ancient wisdom tradition. Whether we see ourselves as combinations of Transport, Conversion, and Structure -- or of Vata, Pitta, and Kapha -- each of us is a shifting and individualized balance of these energies. It's a balance that needs to be continuously acknowledged, understood, and cared for.

As the forces of nature interact within each of us, some of us have more Transport, others are strongest in Conversion, and still others are dominated by Structure. There are even a few individuals who have an almost equal presence of each. The varying proportion of these forces is one of the most essential ways in which we are different from each other.

Initially, you need to identify your own Natural System State. Once this has been done, the goal of supporting that state becomes possible. So what is your essential nature? Which forces give direction to your being? The questions below provide you an intuitive way of understanding your Natural System State. At the website yourbodyyoursystem.com, you can also use the online tool to help you discover your Natural System State.

Are you dominated by the force of Transport?

Transport expresses itself as sensitivity to variations in flow, mobility, and movement. If Transport is your dominant force and that force is too high, you may feel nervous and agitated. If it's too low, you could feel very lethargic or depressed. Transport is in charge of everything that moves and is kinetic in our bodies, including the flow of energy and information. Because of this, Transport is regarded as the primary force without which Conversion or Structure could not function.

When Transport is not functioning correctly, all the other forces can go awry.

396

- Are you extremely uncomfortable in cold weather?
- Do you often juggle several activities at once?
- Do you think and talk quickly?
- Do you prefer spontaneity over scheduling?
- Do you tend toward dry skin and hair?
- Are you naturally thin, and do you lose weight easily?
- Do you grasp new ideas quickly, but wish you could remember more of what you learn?
- Do you impulsively start working on projects without thinking them through?
- Do you sometimes skip meals or forget to eat?
- Are you basically optimistic and enthusiastic?

Are you dominated by the force of Conversion?

Conversion manifests as sensitivity to variations in physiological processes such as metabolism and digestion, as well as analytical thinking and decision-making. If the forces of Conversion are not functioning well, you can experience health and emotional problems associated with the inability to convert and transform elements of Matter, Energy and Information.

- Do you very strongly dislike hot weather?
- Are you detail oriented and exceptionally good at processing information and data?
- Do you think things through before taking action?
- Do you metabolize food quickly and efficiently?
- Do view competition as an enjoyable challenge?
- Does your weight fluctuate?

- Do you prefer to have meals on a set schedule?
- Do you become impatient with yourself or others?
- Do you enjoy turning ideas into applications?
- Are your eyes especially sensitive to sunlight?

Are you dominated by the force of Structure?

Structure is the principle of containment for matter, information, and energy. Men and women who are Structure dominant are naturally able to sustain and tolerate more than other people. Structure forces foster relaxation and calm, and an aura of security. But when Structure is out of balance it can manifest as stubbornness or isolation.

- Do you have a broad body frame?
- Do you tend to be overweight?
- Do you prefer not to move around or travel?
- Are you often called upon to help others?
- Are you not bothered by either hot or cold weather?
- Do you have exceptionally good physical stamina?
- Is your preferred learning style slow and steady?
- Do you easily retain what you've learned?
- Do you take your time moving between activities?
- Do you often have sinus infections or colds?
- Do you try to speak precisely and emphatically?

CHAPTER 11

The Body's Disturbances

Obstacles are part of any journey, including the journey of our lives. Once you become aware of your Natural System State, it's your responsibility to keep that state in balance, despite any turbulence you encounter.

But at any given moment you are likely not operating at the peak of your Natural System State. So how are you right now? How are you feeling today? Is everything going well in your life? Do you feel upbeat and cheerful or do you feel down in the dumps? Are you feeling healthy? Or are you catching a cold?

As a unique and dynamic person, you are not going to be feeling the same every day. Here are some questions to help you get a handle on what the forces of Transport, Conversion, and Structure are doing in your system right now, today. Your answers will help you determine which forces are "off-course." You can then decide how you want to bring that force back into alignment.

Are your Transport forces undergoing disturbances?

- Have you been feeling anxious or overly excited?
- Is your energy level noticeably uneven?
- Are you feeling depressed, or do you have bursts of energy so intense that you have a hard time calming down?
- Do you have any dry spots, chapped, or cracked skin?
- Is your lower GI tract upset? Are you having bouts of diarrhea or constipation? Do you experience gas or bloating?
- Are you forgetting to eat, or are you losing weight?
- Is cold weather bothering you more than usual?
- Are you having difficulty concentrating or finishing projects?
- Are you having joint or arthritic pain?
- Have you been making any impulsive decisions?
- Do you have trouble falling asleep or staying asleep?

Are your Conversion forces undergoing disturbances?

- Are you putting pressure on yourself or others?
- Are you having upper GI problems?
- Are you suffering from heartburn or a sore throat that your doctor thinks is caused by acid reflux?
- Is an aversion to heat becoming more intense?
- Do you need stronger sunglasses than previously?
- Are you easily angered or often impatient?
- Have you become noticeably critical of others?

- Do you drink large amounts of water or other beverages?
- Do you have more rashes or cold sores than usual?
- Do you have feelings of jealousy or a need to get even?

Are your Structure forces undergoing disturbances?
- Are you having sinusitis, allergies, or congestion?
- Are you able to keep your weight under control?
- Do you crave carbs, chocolate, or other sweets?
- Do you want to sleep all the time?
- Do you have a white coat on your tongue?
- Are you generally feeling lethargic and dull?
- Do you often procrastinate?
- Do you accumulate things you don't need?
- Are you finding it difficult make changes in your life?
- Do you respond to stress with hostility?

By learning which forces are disturbed, you can be the Controller, making adjustments to Inputs that will bring you back to your Natural System State. But the first step is to correctly assess what's wrong. What is the true nature of the disturbance? Be real. Don't look for an easy answer, neither in reductionist science nor reassuring mysticism.

CHAPTER 12

Guiding Yourself to Health

Now, given that you know your body's inherent Goal and the Disturbances that perturb it from that Goal, you are ready to figure out the right Inputs, with intelligence, to adjust the forces of Transport, Conversion and Structure so that you can bring your body back and maintain its Natural System State, so it can be in the most optimal state for health and well-being.

Based on the Disturbances you identified to either Transport, Conversion and/or to Structure, you can now feedback in the right Inputs into your system to perform the necessary adjustments. The three sub-sections below are organized to help you figure out the right Inputs.

Controlling the Forces of Transport. Transport is expressed through movement. When it's in balance, Transport presents itself as joy, grace, agility and enthusiasm. Both systems theory and Siddha identify three Inputs as essential for Transport to function at an optimal level: warmth, rhythm and lubrication.

Stay Warm

Our bodies, particularly our muscles, work far more efficiently when they are warmed up before any kind of activity or exercise. Muscles contract and relax faster when they are warm. Warmth gives your muscles greater agility, speed, and strength. Warming up is like an insurance policy, decreasing the possibility of injury while also allowing you a greater degree of motion. If you are warm, your blood vessels are dilated, and this reduces stress on your heart and increases the flow (movement) of blood throughout your body. Blood is the key transporter of nutrients in your body. When you stay warm, your blood is able to be more efficient and deliver more oxygenated blood, making your entire system more effective to support motion at multiple levels. It also enables oxygen in your blood to be transported at a greater speed.

Your joints are key to movement and motion. Staying warm enables you to have a wide range of motion. Stiffness, for example, is a symptom that Transport is not working right. Warmth increases production of synovial fluids in your joints, serving to reduce friction, to support that range of motion. Greater range of motion gives you the greater confidence to try new things in a safe manner. Staying warm helps your body secrete the hormones that enable energy production, which is key to Transport. Exhaustion is another symptom telling us that the forces of Transport are not functioning right.

Movement can be erratic and chaotic, methodical and elegant, or graceful and intelligent. Staying warm enables nerve impulses to be transported at greater speeds, resulting in greater focus. This focus in turn will support the right level of concentration in a relaxed manner to provide support for graceful motion.

In order to thrive, Transport needs the Input of warmth. Think about your car on the coldest winter morning. Most of us will go out and warm it up before driving off. The warmth we are talking about is inner warmth, inside of the engine, inside of the car, inside of you. Warm friends, a warm home, and a warm disposition all fuel your inner forces of Transport. By doing those things that build such inner warmth, you directly support the optimal functioning of Transport.

Stay in Rhythm

A sense of rhythm is the ability to move your body to a regular beat. Rhythm or regularity is key to optimal motion and Transport. A person who dances well moves to a regular rhythm. A great drummer follows a great beat. Musicians often train with a metronome, an instrument that puts out a constant beat, to help them keep their rhythm. One of my mentors Frank Zane, the great body builder, taught me to lift weights to a metronome, or to a beat. When one does this, it makes it much easier, and more fluid. One can move and Transport with greater ease.

Because the force of Transport drives so many important body processes, it requires this level of regularity. Breathing, digestion and elimination are all dependent on proper rhythm and regularity. Having a regular schedule, eating at regular times, and sleeping and waking regularly is all about being in rhythm, which makes Transport far more effective. As someone said, "repetition is the mother of skill."

Siddha masters recommended that their students follow a schedule--early to bed, early to rise, routinized mealtimes, and play and work at particular hours. They were very demanding about the need for such regularity. In fact, in all spiritual practices, regularity is more important than the length of practice. Some people will meditate for 2 hours for a few weeks, and then stop, without any semblance of discipline. It is better to do less, but with consistency to achieve the best results. The highest level of rhythm and regularity is critical for the force of Transport.

In our breathing, the forces of Transport manifest themselves most clearly. Without breath, our entire being ceases to exist. In the Bible, it is said that life began when God breathed into Adam's nostrils. The breath we have has a rhythm and regularity. That rhythm regularizes our pulse, our heart beat and our nerves. Emotions such as anger change our rhythm, and affect the forces of Transport. Every time we move or exercise, it is an exercise in breath. Breath is a gateway for us to see the force of Transport in action, and a way to measure our regularity moment to moment.

Stay Lubricated

Smooth and agile motion is supported by lubrication. All machines move better when they are well lubricated. Think about it. Your car will not move without oil and regular oil changes. Neither will you. To support Transport, your body needs to be well lubricated. Lubrication supports our joints, enables cellular motion, lessens buildup of plaque in our arteries, and ensures that nerve impulses fire right.

Across a range of internal cellular processes, Transport needs lubrication. Without lubrication, the machinery of our bodies begin to squeak, get tight, rust, and motion stops. That squeaking door in your kitchen needs some oil. The stiffness in your joints would also benefit from some lubrication. Lubrication removes friction and ensures long-life of machinery, including your inner machinery.

The right kinds of oils and fats, and proper hydration support that lubrication. Wonderful research is being done and continues to be done on the value of different kinds of wholesome plant and animal based fats and oils. Doing your own research on them can prove to be invaluable. Healthy fats and oils play an overall role in supporting the forces of Transport. They contribute to an increase in energy and help us gain muscle mass. They also support the functioning of our heart, lungs, brain and digestive organs --- all components involved in Transport. The right lubrication makes our internal motors of motion that move air, blood, electrical signals run with ease and minimal friction. Healthy fats help protect our heart, an important motor-like pump from cardiovascular diseases.

Our bones and skeletal structure keep us moving as we walk and run. Lubrication of the right kinds has been shown to strengthen bone density and reduce incidences of fractures, so as we age, we can still keep moving. Your skin is a major organ of transporting fluids and substances such as hormones, lymph, and water. Hydration, which is a form of lubrication, is key to supporting movement of those fluids and substance to support the forces of Transport.

The right kind of lubrication supports internal cellular signaling, and the right signaling is key to cellular communication. Wrong communication results in illness and disease. Studies repeatedly have shown the value of lubrication at the cellular level to protect against various forms of cancer. Lubrication protects our machinery from rusting --- a process known in chemistry as oxidation.

That bicycle chain in your backyard has oxidized and is rusty. Put some oil on it, clean it up, and it's as good as new. Similarly, oils that are known as anti-oxidants can help remove the "rust" from our internal motors so Transport forces are able to glide smoothly. Nerve signaling, a type of cellular signaling, affects mood disorders. Stress affects nerve signaling and may result in increased depression and anxiety. The right kind lubrication increases levels of serotonin in the body. Serotonin makes people feel good and puts them in a relaxed state. Being relaxed supports agile Transport.

Controlling the Forces of Conversion. The forces of Conversion are expressed as intensity and determination. When three key Inputs are present, Conversion presents itself as enterprising, brave, intelligent, ambitious, confident, and self-disciplined. These three Inputs are essential for Conversion to function at an optimal level: being cool, regulated and clean.

Stay Cool

Intensity doesn't need more intensity. Fighting fire with fire doesn't work here. The process of Conversion does the job of converting Matter, Energy and Information from one form into another. These processes all require "heat." However, in order to operate efficiently, they also need proper cooling.

A nuclear reactor, which is able to convert nuclear fission to thermal energy, is a classic example of Conversion. But a nuclear reactor needs those big cooling towers we see when pictures of reactors are shown. Your hot kitchen needs an exhaust system to keep it cool; your computer needs a fan to keep it cool.

Men and women with rapid metabolism and fiery dispositions – expressions of Conversion in action -- need to stay cool, in both mind and body, to balance their internal engines. Those with Conversion dominance need to look to the external world for ways to input cooling factors. This is different from those with a Transport dominance, who need to Input ways of increasing internal warmth.

Conversion dominant people need to avoid "hot situations" that can cause tempers to flare; they need to learn to "cool down" during those times when the intensity of action (during tough business negotiations for example) becomes too extreme. Staying Cool ensures that you don't over-heat and burn up your internal engines, which are the power sources of Conversion.

Warm-blooded animals sweat (like a human) or pant (like a dog) to dissipate heat through water evaporation. Sometimes it's easy just to cool off by going under a nice shaded tree or get some water on us. Other times it may be good just to take a vacation, "chill out" and go to cooler areas. Sometimes just sitting and watching the sunrise or sunset and other of Nature's beauty can serve to provide the cool to calm down and support the forces of Conversion, to remove the "heat."

Stay Regulated

The forces of Conversion are involved in the process of transformation and transduction. They convert energy from one form to another. The retina in your eyes convert light, electromagnetic radiation, to chemical impulses which are transduced to "see" the world. The engine in your car converts chemical energy to rotational mechanical energy.

This all involves many systematic and interconnected processes that need to be regulated correctly, with great sensitivity, to make sure that the inputs are converted to the right outputs.

If your retina does not transduce correctly, you get a blurred vision. If your car engine's pistons are not regulated with the right mixture of fuel and air to fire correctly, your car's motion could be abrupt with backfiring. All engines need to regulate their activity from action to rest, from focused work to regular maintenance --- in short they need to be in balance across the forces of motion and stillness.

Conversion can create a tendency to push too hard. They gravitate toward being on the go all the time, with extreme activity and little rest. If they don't learn how to regulate their activities, they run the risk of "burning up" and "burning out". Sometimes, this inability to regulate their own internal engines, results in an attempt to control everything, and everybody, in their environment. It would be better for them to learn how to control and regulate their own activities.

It can be difficult for a conversion dominant person to "let go" and relax with themselves and others. Their tongues can become harsh and mean --- an inappropriate way to control a situation, because in reality they are not able to control themselves. Extremes of this out-of-control behavior include throwing tantrums, and becoming manipulative, both of which reflect a lack of self-regulation, which can backfire much like a car engine, whose internal pistons misfire. High performance jet engines are designed to function well. They are able to operate across a wide range of temperatures and altitudes. They can regulate their engine performance across a variety of conditions, can adjust and adapt. Conversion forces require proper regulation to ensure their optimal functioning.

Regulation includes setting bounds of operation. Those who are dominated by Conversion forces can achieve great success if they are given, or create for themselves, internal and external boundaries. A high performance car also has its boundaries; if you "red-line" above a certain number of RPM's, the engine will conk out. The forces of Conversion operate well within their lower and upper bounds.

Work and rest are therefore equally important for these forces of Conversion. Forces of Conversion, like a motor can "be on" all the time, and not know when to stop. Men and women with strong Conversion forces have a tendency to overdo just about everything. They can work too hard, they can exercise too much, and they can over-do it with their attention to detail. Our Conversion dominant friends sometimes need to relax and stop competing. They need to learn to modulate their behavior, keeping everything more reasonable and moderate.

Regulating your behavior also implies being able to "surrender" and "go with flow" at appropriate times. Those with dominant Conversion forces can sometimes appear always to be on "high alert" in terms of a need to control the people and things in their environment. They need to learn how to regulate their behavior by stepping back and surrendering. It's essential to know when to stop, relax, rest, and shut down.

Stay Clean

Like any high performance engine, forces of Conversion thrive in a clean environment. This includes both high quality fuel and a clean internal mechanism. People dominated by Conversion need to be very careful about what they input into their bodies. Whole foods -

organic, without preservatives, and without additives - are wonderful because they provide "clean" fuel.

There is an emerging movement among pioneering food manufacturers in formalizing the definition of such clean foods through a newly developed Certified C.L.E.A.N. international standard, which I helped to facilitate using a systems-based approach that defines such foods as ones that have multiple attributes including being safe, non-GMO, organic, and having high bio-availability of nutrients. Keeping an eye out for such clean foods can serve to support Conversion.

Food combining is another wise strategy for ensuring effective transformation within our digestive systems. Slow-cooked foods, in many ways pre-digested, make it easy for our internal engine to absorb nutrients. In addition, regular and moderate fasts allow our engines to clean and heal themselves by supporting the body's own self-healing processes.

Controlling the Forces of Structure

Structure brings stability, and stability is essential for survival. Men and women in whom Structure is dominant tend to have stability in their own lives and they like to provide it for others as well. The three Inputs that encourage Structure's optimal performance are: being dry, active and flexible.

Stay Dry

The force of Structure provides containment and support. When a home is built, the foundation represents the Structure force that holds the entire house. If the foundation (or basement) is damp or wet, the building's entire infrastructure is at risk.

Excessive dampness in your body's foundation can show up as cysts, tumors, chronic sinus infections, and yeast infections. Dryness can also have the benefit of slightly raising the body's temperature, creating a structural environment that is resistant to viruses and bacteria. A dry sauna, for example, can be ideal for supporting Structure.

Stay Active

Use it or lose it. Any physical structure, including the human body, gets stronger the more it gets used and stimulated. If you don't use your muscles, your skeletal structure, you atrophy. Structures that are not used are vulnerable to decay and rust. Various types of stimuli are critical in keeping a structure activated.

At the cellular level, the cell membrane and cytoskeleton support structure of the entire cell. Nature ensures that this structure is under constant stimuli to keep it vigilant and active so it supports the cell structure. Such activity increases the number of macrophages. Macrophages enhance the immune system and support structure by killing invading bacteria and viruses.

Physical activity also increases blood flow, allowing antibodies to move through your system and attack and remove bacteria and viruses. For those who suffer from inflammation, anti-inflammatory cytokines, which are the cell-to-cell signaling molecules, are themselves activated by physical activity. These molecules have a beneficial effect in promoting anti-inflammatory effects. This is one of the important benefits that come from being active because chronic inflammation causes most of the degenerative diseases such as cancer.

The forces of Structure provide framework and inertia. This inertia can also result at its extremes in laziness, moodiness, and immobility. Sometimes those who are dominant in the forces of Structure "just don't feel like moving." Inertia and a lack of movement can contribute to a sense of depression or lethargy. Exercise and physical activity stimulates neurotransmitters in the brain to make one feel happier, less moody, and less depressed. Inertia is also implicated in osteoporosis, a structural disorder that causes bone loss. Exercise and physical activity is prescribed as a treatment for those who have osteoporosis or are in danger of getting it because it can help prevent and arrest the problem.

In order to hold things, Structure itself requires containment. The tendency to "holding on" often spells out issues with weight. Being active is a great controlling and modulating factor to manage one's weight. There is no better cure for the inertia and laziness of Structure forces than to boost one's energy level through physical activity. Diseases such as diabetes manifest when the forces of Structure go to their extremes of containment. Being active can help deal with this condition. Activity helps makes the body more sensitive to insulin, to support burning of glucose e.g. calories. This helps to lower blood glucose and stop sugar spikes. Diabetics who exercise have been shown to need less insulin or medication than those who don't.

People with Structure dominance can also become too complacent and reliant on the status quo. They have a tendency to not want to "let go" of anything, including relationships and objects. They can "hold on" to relationships, situations, and things that no longer have value in their lives. Activity—getting out in the world, meeting new people, and trying new things—is a way of fighting this tendency.

Stay Flexible

Structure contains the elements of water and earth. Structures composed of water and earth can get stuck, muddy, swampy, and immobile. The most powerful structures in the world are not rigid, but flexible. If something is too hard, it can become brittle, and just shatter and break. In civil engineering, when larger structures are built, particularly in earthquake zones, they are designed to sway and to be flexible; sometimes they are even put on rollers, so they will move with the wave of the earthquake. The largest modern skyscrapers in the world now actually flex like pine grass in the wind.

This is a wonderful example of how flexibility can provide additional strength and make structures strong enough to withstand even the most powerful of Nature's forces. Similarly, flexibility is key for someone who is Structure dominant. If you become too stiff, you too can break or fall apart by life's continual and ongoing disturbances and changes. If you become too set in your ways, you might end up feeling as though you are stuck in a quagmire that resembles nothing so much as a muddy swamp.

Flexibility gives structures greater strength. Joints and fascia are particularly improved by flexibility. Blood flow can be increased by flexibility exercises such as stretching, which removes toxins and waste products that can cause a structure to "squeak" and get stiff.

Stretching the joints also results in improved blood flow, which, in turn, can cause slight increases in tissue temperature; this supports circulation and increases the flow of rich nutrients to the joints creating greater elasticity and higher levels of structural performance.

Flexibility allows structures to be more effective in dealing with environmental disturbances. My grandmother used to tell a story of two kinds of trees. One tree would bend when a river flooded and was able to go back to its original shape once the waters receded. The other tree would resist the flood and would ultimately be broken ripped out from its roots. Structures that bend are more likely to survive.

Scientists have repeatedly shown how flexible structures can adjust themselves to reduce drag. It is clear that unlike rigid structures for which an increase in velocity causes a squared increase of drag, the increase in drag for a flexible object is significantly lower.

Above all, it's your responsibility – and your opportunity – to become fully aware of the dominant energies of your being, and your Goal is to keep them in balance to support your Natural System State, not someone else's. Remember too that balance is not a passive state. It's achieved through strong action, and strong action is required to sustain it as well. There's a teaching by Vivekananda, one of India's contemporary spiritual masters, that alludes to this. Despite his metaphysical orientation, Vivekananda advised his students that if there was a choice between doing 50 pushups and meditating for 50 minutes, do the pushups!

PART 4

Your Goal, Your Life

CHAPTER 13

Setting Your Goal

You've learned the difference between an open system and an intelligent system. You've been exposed to several examples of how to apply systems theory to achieve goals in weight management, growing a business and finding a partner. And, you've also learned how your body is a system and how you can use systems theory to bring your body back to its inherent goal of health and well-being.

In this section you'll learn how you can go end-to-end in setting and attaining goals in any area of your life by fine-tuning your sensors and controllers -- and most importantly, by committing to achieve whatever objectives you've chosen, by consistently adjusting the inputs in a process of continual refinement, until the goal is achieved.

In setting any goal, the first critical step is your ability to bring all your senses into the process. You must see, smell, hear, taste, and feel the result you want to obtain. I learned how to do this early in life, when I learned Siddha visualization techniques from my grandparents.

When I was twelve years old, I wanted to win my high school's math award, which was given once a year. I was able to envision myself – literally see myself – walking onstage to accept the award. I could hear the applause of the audience. I could feel the award in my hand. I had access to the entire movie of getting that award, which was the Output I wanted to obtain.

This imaginary but extremely vivid experience is something you should train yourself to have when setting your Goal. It is critical to success and you must involve all your senses. Once you're able to do that in your mind (the Manas in Siddha or the Controller in modern systems theory), you'll be surprised by how much easier it becomes to reach your goal in the physical world.

Exercise 1

Here's the first exercise, which you can do right now.

Step 1: Find a chair to seat in and close your eyes. Take ten deep breaths and relax.

Step 2: Now, simply observe your breath, your natural rhythm of inhaling and exhaling. This is an excellent way to enter a relaxed state of mind. Do this for 5 minutes.

Step 3: Once you're in that relaxed state, envision your goal and use all your senses to connect yourself with that vision. See the goal. Feel it. Hear it. Touch it. Even smell it, when appropriate (like making that tasty soup).

Step 4: Let yourself remain in this visionary state for ten or fifteen minutes, and then gradually re-orient yourself to your actual physical setting.

Step 5: Now, take a pen and paper and write a description of what you've just experienced, and make that description as detailed as possible.

Research has shown this exercise to be extremely effective. One well-known study focused on shooting basketball free throws. The subjects of the study were high school basketball players, who were divided into two randomly selected groups. Over the course of several days, one group practiced physically shooting free throws for twenty minutes each day. The other group simply visualized shooting free throws, with the stipulation that each visualized shot had to be a perfect swish.

In the final phase of the study, the two groups shot a certain number of actual free throws. It turned out that both groups had improved their accuracy from the start of the research – and the visualization group had improved just as much as the players who had taken actual shots.

The effect of thinking was as great as the effect of actually doing. But it needs to be more than just thinking. It needs to be seeing, feeling, touching, hearing, and smelling.

Exercise 2

Here's another technique that I learned from my grandparents that you can do just before you go to sleep.

Step 1: Lie in bed face up with your eyes closed, and with your hands at your side.

Step 2: Take 10 deep breaths and relax.

Step 3: Place the middle finger of your right hand on your forehead between your eyebrows, just slightly above the level of your eyes, and gently tap it three times. In Siddha, that point is known as the third eye.

Step 4: Remembering that point, observe the rhythm of your breathing as you visualize the achievement of your goal, from Exercise 1, on the blank screen of your third eye.

Step 5: As you are visualizing your goal, if you get distracted, gently either use your breath to bring you back to the visualization or use a mantra by saying or whispering a word or phrase that has special value for you, to remind you to come back to that vision.

If your mind starts to wander, gently re-focus your attention. You're literally programming your mind to connect with your goal at multiple levels. There are great benefits from doing this every night just before you fall asleep.

Remember that all Goals have challenges. Every objective gives rise to Disturbances. We've seen how working through Disturbances is an essential element of systems theory. As soon as possible, you should make yourself as aware of Disturbances – both potential ones and present ones – just as you've done with other elements of your system.

Exercise 3

Lists are good things. You should make a list of the top 5 Disturbances that will get in the way of your Goal:

1._____

2._____

3._____

4._____

5._____

This list provides you those things that you will have to consciously either avoid interacting with or ones for which you will have to use your mind and support system to find solutions to overcome them.

CHAPTER 14

Knowing Your Sensors and Controller

As we learned from the characters in Part Two, the process of achieving a goal depends on several components in your system. You need accurate and reliable sensors, and you need an effective controller.

Let's focus on the sensors. Once you've set your goal, you need to immediately find measurable ways of determining whether you're on course, toward the Outputs. The important point here is that these Outputs must be measureable and something that is tangible and concrete --- meaning Sensors can sense them and measure them with clarity and accuracy.

For example, if your goal is to get a new high-paying and rewarding job, you should write down the measurable Outputs that make that job attractive for you. These could include the salary, the location and the kinds of benefits. Now you will need the right Sensors to measure this.

You need to be very clear regarding the Output you're seeking. It's not enough to say, "I want a great job" The meaning of a great job has to be finely tuned and measurable.

You need the Sensors that can precisely measure the Output features of the companies that you're considering. Google Maps, for instance, could probably be a reliable Sensor for information on the distance factor - how far is the job from your home. Asking the HR person to provide you the range of salary for the job and a detailed list of benefits offered by the company is a way for you to know what you're getting into. That is the Sensor facility in action.

Now, for your Goal, let's do this next exercise so you know your Outputs and how you are going to measure them.

Exercise 4

For your goal, list the five top Outputs, measureable things that help you know if you are on target to achieve your goal. Next to each Output, write down what you will use (the Sensor) to measure that Output.

Measurable Outputs   Sensors

1._____

2._____

3._____

4._____

5._____

For example, if your goal is to lose weight. One Output can be your current weight. The Sensor for that would be a bathroom scale that lets you measure your weight. Another Output can be the circumference of your hips. The Sensor for that would be a tape measure.

For the job example, you may write something like this down:

Output	Sensor
1. Salary	1. Offer letter
2. Distance for home	2. Google maps
3. Maternity leave	3. Company policy manual
4. Dental insurance	4. Health benefits brochure
5. Corporate atmosphere	5. Check on websites like Glassdoor to see how former employees have evaluated it

Once, you've figured out your Output and Sensors, you can use your Controller (your mind) to: 1) compare whether the current Output matches your goal, and 2) make decisions on what new Inputs/Actions/Karma you are going to take to move towards your goal.

Exercise 5

In this respect, begin by taking account of your actual Goal relative to the current output. Suppose you just had an interview, you can use this table to make such a rational assessment where on the left side you list the five key elements of your Goal, and on the right side you list the five actual features (the Output) of the current job prospect.

Goal	Output
1.	1.
2.	2.
3.	3.
4.	4.
5.	5.

For example, using the job example, you may come up with a list like this:

Goal	Output
1. Salary:$100,000	1. $75,000
2. Distance for home: 30 mi.	2. 15 mi.
3. Maternity leave: Yes	3. Yes
4. Dental insurance: Yes	4. No
5. Corporate atmosphere: Excellent	5. Yes

So measuring the difference between the Goal and the Output, is one aspect of the Controller. The other aspect is to make decisions. This begins by itemizing

428

what actions we are going to take given the situation at hand. For your Goal, given the results of Exercise 5, write down the top 5 actions you are now going to do to change the course of your Output so get to your Goal:

Inputs/Actions/Karma

1._____

2._____

3._____

4._____

5._____

Using the job example from above, we see that 3 out of the 5 items of our Goal are being achieved from the most recent job interview. What is "off course" is that we are $25,000 off in salary and we have no Dental insurance. So now the actions we can take would be enumerated as follows:

Inputs/Actions/Karma

1. Negotiate for a higher salary

2. Research Dental Insurance costs

3. Go for a different job interview

4. Accept the offer

These are the four Inputs/Actions we can take. We may find that the cost of Dental Insurance is nominal and we may foot the bill ourselves. Alternatively, we may find a good salary negotiating coach who can mentor us to help negotiate a higher salary or we may simply go for a different interview.

The point is that this is an iterative and rational process. No magic here. Remember that the basic function of a Controller is to develop a strategy based on information the Sensors provide about a company, as well as what you have to offer. If the Sensors disclose a clear disconnect between your Goal and the Output coming from a company, your Controller's strategy should involve either adjusting the Goal or moving on to apply at a different firm.

On the other hand, the Sensor might reveal that a company's Outputs are in line with your Goals – but your resume clearly does not meet the employer's requirements. Your Controller will integrate the conflicting factors. One strategy might involve looking for work for which you're qualified. Another strategy could be getting further education or experience to strengthen your resume.

The bottom line is this. Use the elements of systems theory to take control of your life. Set your goals, get information from your Sensors, develop strategies through your Controller -- and then act on what you've learned.

CHAPTER 15

Commitment Not Perfection

Now you know your Goals, you know your Outputs, you know your Disturbances, and you know your Inputs. Based on all this, you will move forward by changing yourself or changing the environment around you. You're going to change the forces of Transport, Conversion, and Structure within you, or you're going to change the forces that are external to you.

You have powerful forces on your side. But even with that power, don't make perfection your primary focus. That focus should be on commitment. Without commitment, nothing can be achieved – because you'll need to traverse the feedback loop as many times as it takes. That's the nature of intelligent systems, and commitment is the basis of reaching goals through those systems.

Commit to observing your Outputs. Commit to looking clearly at your Goals. Commit to refining your Controller on an ongoing basis.

You may need to remove or improve some of your Sensors. Make a commitment to knowing when that needs to happen, and to getting it done.

This will affect the forces of Transport, Conversion, and Structure within your consciousness and also in the physical realities of your life. Commit to making that happen and to embracing the results.

Altering Transport, for example, could mean that you'll need to move differently during the day. You might need to move more quickly, or you might need to learn to sit still. Altering Transport could mean moving to a different house or apartment, or even to a different part of the country. Be ready to make that commitment when you first start using systems theory.

You may need to change the people who are around you in order to gain inspiration from friends. Or you may need to become more inspirational and proactive yourself. All this pertains to Transport.

Write down three examples of Transport that will be needed in order to attain your Goal? What are you going to need to change?

What about the forces of Conversion? Commit to identifying information from your Sensors and converting that information into action. You may not be able to do this entirely on your own. If you need an effective resume, you might not be a good enough writer to convert your education and experience into words on a page. So commit to finding someone who can help you with that conversion, or who can do it for you. If you're like most people, you might need a good accountant or financial advisor. That may cost some money, so commit to paying what it costs.

For most people, the Conversion element means bringing in other people who can help you turn your weak points into strong points. Don't let pride or self-consciousness stop you from making that commitment. Very few successful people can do everything on their own. In fact, some successful people can hardly do anything on their own, so they commit themselves to getting help.

Those helpers are not necessarily employees or subordinates. Often they're people who are older and more experienced – experts, or mentors. Think of some specific people who can play that part in your life.

Make a commitment also to building an effective structure in your life. Structure doesn't mean rigidity. It's really a combination of strength and flexibility. A good way to start enhancing Structure in your life is to take up activities that support strength and flexibility in very physical ways. Anything from yoga to weight lifting can serve that purpose. Meditation and mindful practices can improve emotional and spiritual structure. Those activities require discipline, so make a commitment to supplying that discipline.

Printed by Amazon Italia Logistica S.r.l.
Torrazza Piemonte (TO), Italy